FIRST AID FOR HORSES

VANESSA BRITTON

WARD LOCK

A WARD LOCK BOOK

First published in the UK in 1995 by Ward Lock
Wellington House, 125 Strand, London WC2R 0BB

A Cassell Imprint

Distributed in the United States
by Sterling Publishing Co., Inc.
387 Park Avenue South, New York, NY 10016-8810

Distributed in Australia
by Capricorn Link (Australia) Pty Ltd
2/13 Carrington Road, Castle Hill, NSW 2154

A British Library Cataloguing in Publication Data
block for this book may be obtained from the British Library

ISBN 0-7063-7294-8

Typeset by Litho Link Ltd, Welshpool, Powys, Wales

Printed and bound in Great Britain by
Hillman Printers (Frome) Ltd

Frontispiece: *If your horse goes lame, have him trotted up to see if you can pinpoint the trouble.*

FIRST AID FOR HORSES

CONTENTS

INTRODUCTION

Even if you are the most vigilant of owners, endeavouring to provide your horse with a safe environment in which to live, you are more than likely at some stage to find yourself having to cope with an emergency, or a situation that requires immediate action to prevent a more serious situation from developing. That immediate action is 'first aid'.

You might think that the best person to administer first aid would be a veterinary surgeon but very often this is not the case. Sometimes a vet is unavoidably delayed and can take an hour or more to arrive, which means that the best person to administer first aid is the person on the spot – you. The time spent administering first aid while waiting for a vet is often the 'make or break' of a sick horse's recovery, and in a dangerous emergency it could indeed save your horse's life.

Coping with the unexpected is far easier if you know the correct procedures to follow, and this book will give you that information. It will also show you how to keep your horse healthy, how to recognize the signs of ill health and what to do about them.

For serious emergencies, and also whenever you are in doubt about an illness or injury, you will of course call your vet, but everyday cuts and bruises can benefit from your own care, which could prevent the nasty complications that can arise from neglect. You need to know the proper precautions and treatments; you need to acquire the skills to tackle common problems and the knowledge to keep your horse healthy in the first place.

With the help of this book you will not find this too difficult and you will probably refer to it for guidance time and time again. But the book stresses the importance of seeking veterinary advice so that a correct diagnosis can be made and 'second aid' can be carried out.

Second aid is the continuing treatment of an illness with veterinary support. While correct first aid is essential, and while the information in *First Aid for Horses* will help you to keep veterinary bills to a minimum, it does not replace the need for veterinary attention. For the sake of your horse, it is vital that you work *with* your vet.

CHAPTER 1

THE HEALTHY HORSE

Looking after a horse is a great responsibility as well as a pleasure, and sometimes it can all seem a bit daunting. This may be especially true if you haven't grown up around horses or had any formal equestrian training. However, do not despair just yet. The key to a healthy horse is 'knowing your horse', and this is something that does not need scientific qualifications. Getting to know your horse really well is the most important factor in establishing a good relationship. When you come to learn your horse's individual characteristics and little idiosyncrasies, the hours you spend together will be full of joy. Once a strong bond has built up between you, there is little that can break it. If your horse gallops towards you when you call, you will experience the pleasure that horses bring.

If you have taken the time to get to know your horse this well, you will be able to tell within a few minutes of greeting him whether he is feeling well, or not. You will be the first to detect when he is acting oddly; it is like a sixth sense: you may not be able to pinpoint exactly what the problem is, but you will know that he is 'not right'. This sixth sense is a great asset: it can often provide an early warning of more serious illnesses. If you do not really know what constitutes normal behaviour for your horse, then it may take you longer to realize that he is not in full health.

Such early detection may prevent many ailments from turning into more serious conditions if they are treated promptly and correctly. Instant and efficient first aid can produce quicker and superior healing and recovery. Therefore, you should know how to deal with minor ailments and have enough knowledge to cope with the situation until expert help arrives. While this does mean knowing what you should do, it often more importantly means knowing what you should *not* do.

HEALTH CHECKS

Take time each day to have a good look at your horse and frequently give him a health check – remember prevention is always better than cure. Start by simply observing your horse's behaviour and condition. When you have satisfied yourself that all appears to be fine on first observations, you should make a closer physical check to be doubly sure. While this might take a while for the first few times, it will soon become second nature.

Observations

Attitude

While healthy, your horse should always appear bright and cheerful. Even though your particular horse may have a cheeky or perhaps even moody temperament, he should never appear 'sick or sorry'. Alertness is also a good indicator of health. How is the horse standing in the field? If he stands dejectedly on his own or shows any other unusual behaviour, your alarm bells should start to ring: is he feeling off-colour? Many horses will whicker when they see you and will eagerly watch your every move as you approach. Does your horse usually do this? Is he doing so today?

Stance

The healthy horse will stand evenly on all four feet, or might rest a hind foot if feeling particularly relaxed. Most horses stand up during the day, even if they are asleep. However, if yours is lying down he should quickly jump up when he hears you approaching – unless, like some horses, he is so relaxed in your company that he is happy to stay down. It is in this type of situation that knowing your horse is so important. If your horse often lies down when you are around, then there is no need to start panicking.

The healthy horse is bright, alert and in good body condition.

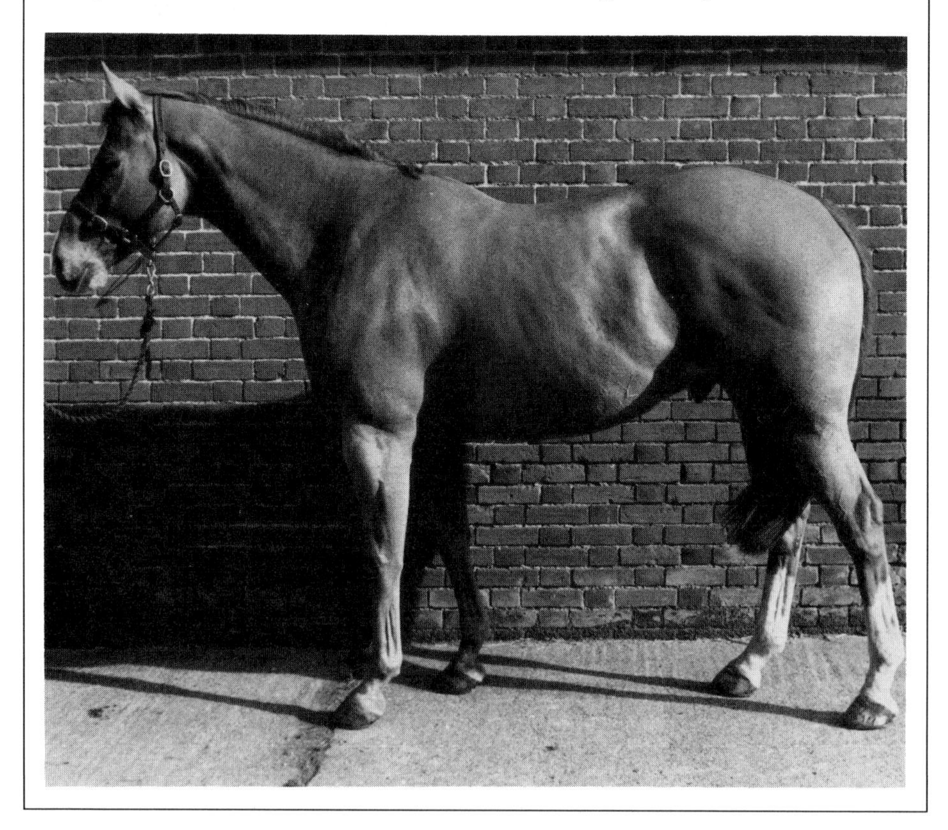

Coat
Horses should have a nice glossy sheen to their coats, unless they live out in winter, when their coats may appear rather dull. Even if you do not have time to give your horse a thorough grooming every day, his coat should still be relatively free from scurf as the natural oils will keep his skin in good condition.

Condition
Your horse's ribs should be reasonably well covered, but not so that he appears fat and stodgy. Horses that are too fat will be as much at risk for health problems as those that are too thin. Run your fingers along the rib cage – you should just be able to feel them.

Appetite
Horses should eat up well, though some individuals are known to be fussy eaters. Food left in the manger should set off warning bells, as appetite is one of the first things to be affected when a horse starts to feel unwell. If your horse suddenly develops a poor appetite it is often a warning that colic or some sort of viral infection is to follow. If you notice (and you should) that your horse frequently drops food from his mouth (known as quidding), or if you see wet balls of food in the manger, there may be a problem with his teeth, and this needs immediate attention before the horse's health starts to suffer as a result.

Droppings
Observation of a horse's droppings is very important. The amount, consistency and colour can provide vital clues to health. When you attend your horse in the mornings, take a look at the droppings. There should be between about four and eight piles. If you cannot see any piles, or far fewer than normal, this may be a warning of an impaction or stoppage of the bowel. Look for signs of colic (see p. 61).

Unless you have recently changed the management of your horse, by turning him out on to fresh grass or feeding him more corn, for example, his droppings should always be the same colour and consistency. They should be neither hard nor wet, like cow-pats, but moist without any foul odour. If the droppings suddenly become soft, you should assume all is not well and investigate further. Droppings like cow-pats may indicate a problem with teeth, a bowel infection or perhaps indigestion caused by worms.

The colour of the droppings will also indicate a horse's state of health. If they become mustard-coloured without any dietary change, then he may have redworm or some liver disorder. If they become coated in mucus, then he may be suffering from an irritation of the gut, possibly caused by inappropriate foods, hay or an infection. If they give off an offensive smell, the problem may be worms or musty hay or feed.

Urine
Your horse's urine will usually be pale, although it may turn slightly darker in summer when he sweats more. If it becomes thick or cloudy, this might indicate some form of digestive imbalance or kidney trouble.

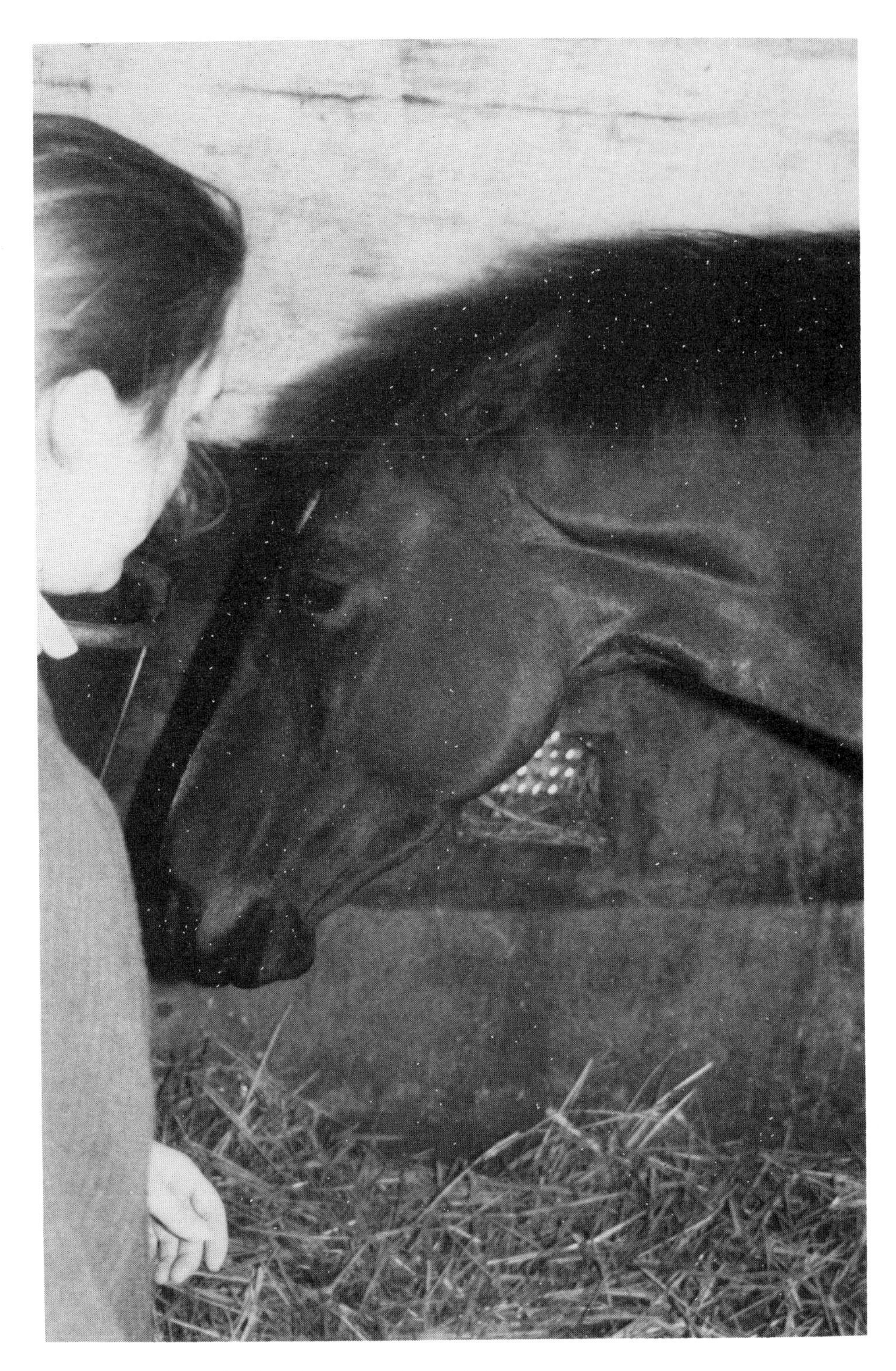

'Know your horse.' Is he always as miserable?

Physical checks

Eyes
A horse's eyes should be bright and focused. Gently turn the eyelids outwards – you should be able to see a nice salmon-pink membrane. It is important to check these while the horse is in good health, so that you know what is normal for that horse. The colour of eye membranes does vary: some horses have paler membranes than others, for example, even when they are perfectly healthy. Unless you know what is normal for your horse, you cannot tell what is *not* normal.

Nostrils
These should be moist, and they too should be a nice salmon-pink colour inside. There should be no thick, yellowish discharges although there are often a few droplets of watery discharge.

Limbs
A horse's limbs should be free from heat or swelling, although some horses do suffer from 'filled legs' (puffy limbs) after being stabled overnight. This may be normal for them but if your horse's legs are usually free from puffiness and they suddenly start to fill, then you should suspect that something is wrong, especially if heat is present. Have your horse trotted up for you; he should put weight evenly on all four feet and the strides should all be of a uniform length. (See Chapter 7)

Skin
This should be supple and easy to 'rock' back and forth on top of the underlying layers. Your horse should feel warm and dry to the touch and the coat should lie flat against the skin. If you pinch the skin (known as the 'pinch test'), it should immediately spring back into place once released. If the pinch remains visible, your horse is showing signs of dehydration.

CHAPTER 2

MAINTAINING GOOD HEALTH

You must have heard the saying that 'prevention is better than cure' and this is very true when managing your horse's health: prevention is cheap, while cure may run into hundreds of pounds in vet bills. It makes sense, for both your horse and your pocket, if you do all that you can to maintain your horse in good health. Always try to bear the following points in mind:

- It is your duty to provide your horse with a *balanced diet* relating to the amount of exercise and the horse's size and metabolism (the total of a horse's chemical and physical activities).
- You should ensure that your horse receives *basic routine care* such as regular worming, vaccinations, foot care and dentistry.

  – Most horses need *worming* every six to eight weeks, although this does depend on individual factors such as whether the horse is stabled or lives at grass with other horses (see p. 31).

  – To protect against equine influenza and tetanus, your veterinary surgeon should *vaccinate* your horse with an initial course, followed by yearly boosters. You will receive a certificate, proving that your horse has been vaccinated, which will be required on entering a show ground if you intend to compete with your horse.

  – Your horse's *teeth* will probably need rasping once a year (see pp. 22–4). More regular check-ups might be needed for a horse that is under 4 or over 16 years old.

  – A horse that is in work will probably need *shoeing* about every five or six weeks. Unshod horses need their hooves trimmed every six to eight weeks.
- You should always allow horses plenty of *time away from the stable.* Turn them out as much as possible. If you have to keep them in for any length of time, try to give them plenty of walks in-hand. While this may prove time-consuming, a horse's mental health will soon start to suffer if he is shut up all day long and this will in turn affect overall health.

Such routine care can reduce the need for first aid or for veterinary attention as the healthy horse is less likely to succumb to disease, infection or injury.

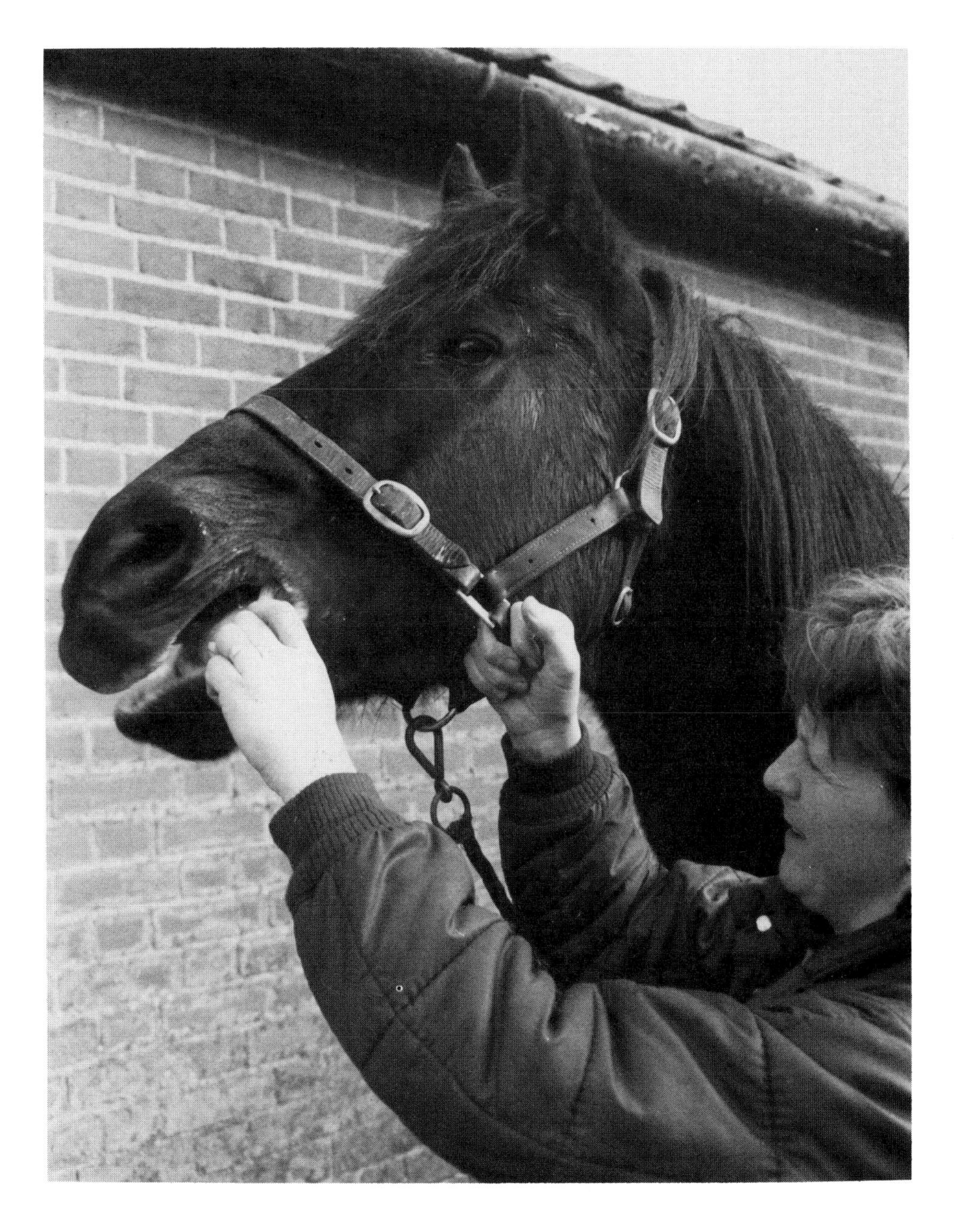

Your horse should receive basic routine care including regular worming.

FEEDING AND EXERCISE

As domesticated animals, horses rely totally on humans to see that they have all they need to stay healthy. If you fail to do the job well, your horse will soon start to deteriorate – but there is no reason for you to fail. Any dedicated horse-owner can achieve the right balance. You need to pay attention to every detail of your horse's everyday management: it is all

To keep horses in good mental health they should always be allowed plenty of freedom from the stable – in all weathers, unless they are ill.

part of the challenge of horse ownership.

So, is your horse being fed and exercised properly?

To start with, you need to work out how much feed your horse should be receiving for the work he is doing. This is not as simple as it sounds: each horse is an individual and it is impossible to lay down firm guidelines. Feeding too little will result in poor condition and loss of energy, while feeding too much may cause the development of conditions such as azoturia (sudden stiffening of the hindlimbs which can be fatal if the horse is walked for any distance) as well as making the horse dangerously obese and badly behaved.

The first step in working out how much to feed is to determine the horse's body weight – ideally on a weighbridge (remember to take your own weight into account if you are holding him). Otherwise use a special weighing-tape for horses, or an ordinary tape-measure.

Using a weighing-tape or girth-tape

You need to take two measurements:
1. The heart girth: measure around the horse just behind the withers.
2. The length: from point of buttocks to point of shoulder.

To find out the horse's body weight in pounds, take the measurements in inches and put them into the following equation:

Body weight (lb) = (heart girth × length) ÷ 241.3

In metric units, take the measurements in centimetres:

Body weight (kg) = (heart girth × length) ÷ 8,717

Once you know the weight, you can begin to calculate how much to feed in relation to the work. The average horse should receive about 2.5 per cent of body weight in feed per day.

Next you need to decide upon a suitable ratio of roughage (forage such as hay or haylage) to concentrates ('hard feeds' such as coarse mixes, cubes, oats etc.) for the horse's workload. Inevitably you will find yourself continually assessing the horse's condition and adjusting the diet accordingly.

Ratio of roughage to concentrates for various work levels

Work level	Roughage %	Concentrates %
At rest	100	0
Light exercise	75	25
Medium work	60	40
Hard work	40	60

SIGNS OF GOOD CONDITION

The best indication of whether you are successfully providing a good, balanced feeding and fitness programme is the horse's appearance. Be guided by his condition. Once you have found a routine that works, do not fiddle around with it.

Make a point of assessing condition every month. When you are with your horse daily, small changes may occur that you might not notice. (It is like watching a baby grow up – you might not be able to see the changes but someone who has not seen the baby for a while notices a huge difference.) If you are uncertain, take your horse's measurements to determine any change. Then do something about it if your horse starts to lose weight or gets fatter.

Viewing a horse from the side can be deceptive as you get a fairly 'flat' picture. Viewing at an angle from behind is better. Horses should be well covered, with no ribs sticking out, and they should be generally nice and round without being obese.

Special considerations

- *Fat horses* are not healthy horses. Their heart and joints will be under stress, particularly when they are worked. It is wise to follow a programme of controlled exercise and diet until the horse loses weight and becomes fitter, when the normal training programme can be resumed.
- '*Good doers*', as long as they are reasonably fed, always seem to keep condition on, whatever their workload.

You should aim to have your horse in the right condition. A horse that is too fat is just as likely to have health problems as a horse that is too thin.

- Horses with *less than perfect conformation* are often more difficult to keep in good condition. No horse is perfect but any obvious faults in conformation (such as a roach back which reduces weight-carrying ability or a neck set too thick, which can affect the horse's wind) may need special consideration for health care.
- *Youngsters* need to be fed carefully. They need enough food to maintain healthy growth, but they must not become too fat as this would put unnecessary strain on their growing joints.
- It is far more difficult to keep *older horses* in good condition. At some point the question of retirement usually arises but there is no need for it as long as the horse is not in pain and still enjoys the work. Indeed many working horses appear to decline far more rapidly if retired.

PREVENTING ACCIDENTS

In order to prevent accidents you need to ensure that the field, the stable, the schooling arena and any ground for riding are as safe as possible.

Field checks:

- Is the fencing safe? (Post-and-rail and thick natural hedges are the safest, but check for any broken rails or gaps).
- Check for any dangerous objects that may be lying in the undergrowth.
- Make sure that none of the other horses in the field are known to be bullies.
- Is the field free of poisonous plants?
- Check that the field has not recently been treated with any chemicals.
- Check that the field is not infested with worms.
- Is there a good supply of clean, fresh water?
- If the field borders any footpaths, put up notices asking people not to feed the horses.

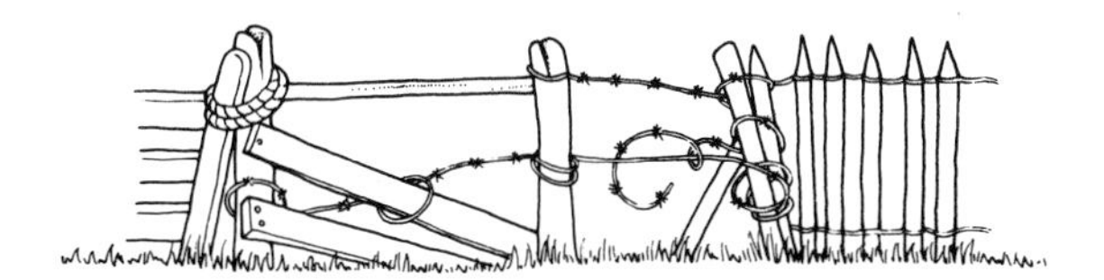

Fencing like this is waiting for an injury to occur.

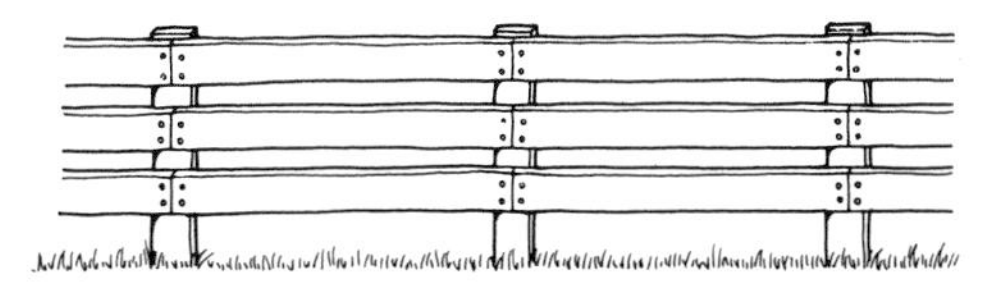

This type of safe fencing will help to prevent injuries.

Stable checks:

- Remove all protruding objects and keep stable fittings to a bare minimum.
- If providing water in buckets, remove the handles so that your horse cannot get his leg caught.
- Ensure that your horse cannot reach any electrical wiring, light bulbs or switches.
- Check that the stable is large enough (if it is too small, your horse may get cast more easily). It should measure a minimum of 3.5m × 3.5m (12ft × 12ft) for a horse, and 3m × 3m (10ft × 10ft) for a pony.

Schooling and riding checks:

- Put on protective boots to prevent your horse banging his legs together or on fences.
- To prevent injuries such as saddle sores, make certain that the tack fits and has been adjusted for maximum comfort.
- Make every effort to check the ground upon which you are riding. Think ahead: does that nice stretch of green grass in the distance have any pot-holes in it? Walk along it first to check before having a canter.

THE FIRST AID KIT

A good and complete first aid kit is the most essential piece of equipment for any yard or horsebox, and everybody concerned should always know exactly where to find it.

In order to cope with the day-to-day responsibilities of administering first aid when necessary, you should have a properly equipped first aid kit and a back-up medicine cupboard. While bandages and dressings can be improvised in an emergency, it is preferable to have everything to hand that you might need, so that you are prepared for most eventualities.

Make a checklist of your kit's contents, so that it is easy to see what has been used and therefore what you need to replace – *today*.

A well-stocked first aid kit

The first aid kit should always be well stocked and ready to hand.

There are commercial kits on the market which contain all you might need for instant first aid, in their own carrying cases, and these are ideal when travelling. However, you can make up your own kit, which should consist of:

1. A 30cm (12in) roll of gauze and cotton tissue: absorbent wadding for infected and discharging wounds, which also provides leg support.
2. Two packets of poultice dressing to reduce swelling and draw out infection.

3. Veterinary antiseptic spray: for the treatment of superficial wounds.
4. Veterinary wound powder: for use on minor wounds, sores, cuts, bites and scratches.
5. Waterproof sticking plaster: for securing bandages.
6. Bandages, 50mm and 75mm (2in and 3in) wide: for securing dressings and providing support.
7. A packet of antiseptic lint: for use on open wounds.
8. A jar of ordinary salt: which can be used diluted with water as a wash and to help harden skin.
9. A packet of Epsom salts: which can be used as a laxative.
10. Vaseline: for use when taking a horse's temperature.
11. A small bottle of iodine: which can be used to counter irritants.
12. A cold pack: for application to bruised or damaged tendons.
13. Disposable syringes and sterile needles: for use when injections are needed.
14. A tube of antiseptic skin ointment: for use on wounds, sores and bites.
15. A veterinary thermometer: to take the horse's temperature.
16. A pair of scissors: which should be sharp, but blunt-ended, for cutting away hair from the edges of wounds or cuts that need dressing and for cutting the dressing itself.

Make sure your storage container is secure and that everything within is recorded on the lid. Large airtight plastic containers with snap-on lids are excellent for use and once stocked should be stored on a shelf away from children, dogs, stable cats and mice, in a cool, dry area. Endeavour to make yourself familiar with all the items in the kit and learn their correct uses. Most will have recommendations for use on their labels, but if in doubt ask your veterinary surgeon to explain anything which seems confusing – before you ever need to use it.

Every time you have cause to use something from your kit you should replace it *immediately*, as you never know how soon you will need it again. Certain items such as medicines, creams and lotions can go out of date, so check them periodically and replace when necessary. Also check that the seals on sterile materials are intact: if they are not, the materials should not be used.

Having a first aid kit at the ready and knowing how to use it properly is one of the best things you can do for your horse. Correct, immediate action can often save minor injuries from turning nasty and in extreme cases can even save lives.

PREVENTING DISEASE

Diseases can often be prevented. Routine vaccinations will help, but all the other horses in a yard should be vaccinated as well. Rules of cleanliness and good hygiene should always be observed. During grooming, for example, having wiped a horse's dock with a clean sponge, do not then use the same sponge on the eyes and nostrils. Deal with minor ailments, such as scurfy skin, as soon as they appear, to prevent them turning into nastier conditions.

Good stable management is of paramount importance, as poor management is known to be a major contributing factor to the origin and spread of many diseases. If your horse does suffer from an ailment, ask yourself if it could have been avoided. It might not make you feel too good if truthfully your answer has to be yes, but it will prevent you from making the same mistake again.

PREVENTING SUFFERING

In order to prevent suffering, be vigilant. Do not wait until a problem is staring you in the face before you become aware of it: be on the look-out for it. Continually evaluate your horse each day in all situations. Ask yourself:

- Is my horse his normal self today?
- Has anything which happened yesterday affected him?
- Are his nose and eyes free from discharge?
- Is his skin free from sores?
- Are his feet and limbs in good order?
- Are his shoes on tight?
- Is he quite happy and sound when I ride him?
- Is he sweating unusually?
- Is he eating up?

CARING FOR YOUR HORSE'S TEETH

It is your responsibility to ensure that your horse does not suffer any unnecessary pain in the mouth and that the teeth last for a lifetime. At the very least, neglected teeth can cause your horse pain; at worst there may be a need for dental surgery, which is both expensive and formidable – there are problems with access, for example, and the teeth are very firmly attached to the jaw so that their removal is a major undertaking. Minimize potential problems by keeping an eye on the condition of your horse's mouth, and ensure that he is seen regularly by a knowledgeable person so that developing problems are identified and action is swiftly taken.

Many problems are concealed, and poor performance or condition caused by tooth trouble tends to creep up gradually, so that you might not be aware of it unless you check for problems regularly. It is understandable that you might shy away from routinely inspecting your horse's mouth; after all, a horse's teeth are large and numerous, which may give rise to thoughts of a nasty bite. Additionally, some horses do not like having their mouths inspected and may give you a hard time when you try to do so.

Rasping

Horse's teeth are not at all like ours and consequently need different treatment. The problem is not one of cavities, but of sharpness. Equine teeth are continually growing through the gum and are then worn

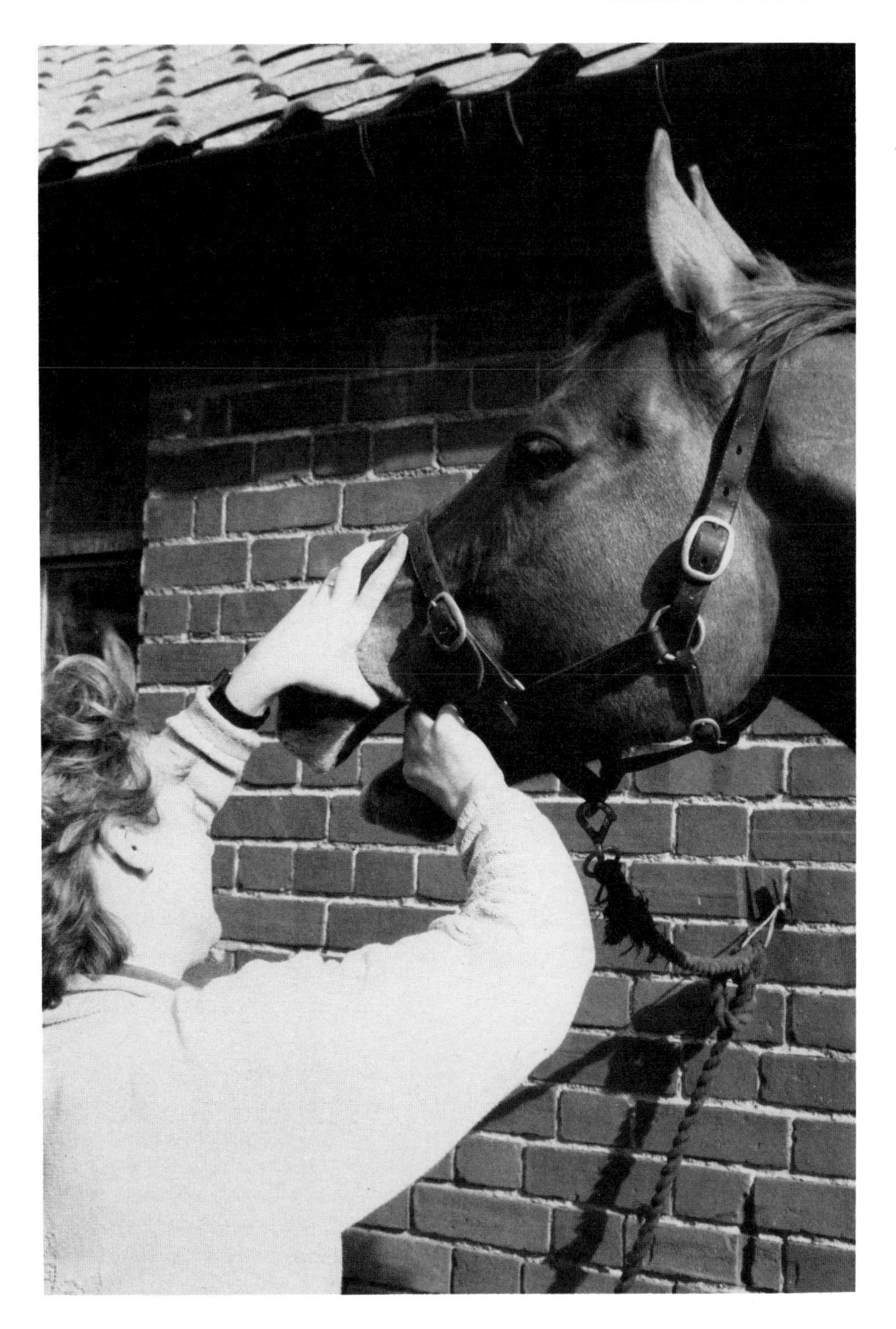

It is your responsibility to ensure your horse is not suffering from pain in the mouth due to sharp teeth, or some other problem.

down by grinding on food. As a result, they regularly form sharp edges on the outside of the upper teeth and the inside edges of the lower teeth, which can become painful if not attended to.

Each horse's jaw and chewing pattern is slightly different and, as with all other aspects of health care, you need to establish what is normal for your horse and how often attention is needed. Some horses will go for two years and still have nice smooth teeth, while others will develop sharp teeth after only a few months from the last rasping.

It is possible to check a horse's teeth for signs of sharpness from the outside. Feel the cheek where the ridge of teeth juts out and firmly run your fingers down the line of teeth. You may not feel a sharp edge, but if a horse objects to the finger pressing it is a good indication that the teeth need rasping and perhaps that the horse's cheek is sore.

Other signs which may indicate that a horse's teeth need attention include:

- Quidding (where the horse continually drops food from the mouth while eating).
- Slow eating.
- Loss of condition, which could be as a result of improperly chewed food.
- Whole grains of food in the droppings.
- Signs of impaction colic.
- Ridden evasions such as nodding, leaning on one rein, going behind or above the bit and, in more severe cases, rearing, napping and bolting.

Tooth-rasping is not a job you can do yourself: it takes a great deal of knowledge and expertise. Ask either your veterinary surgeon or someone who is experienced at tooth-rasping and has been highly recommended by a reliable source. Always consult your veterinary surgeon if there are any signs of disease in the mouth.

CARING FOR YOUR HORSE'S EYES

Eyes are another part of the horse's anatomy which you might shy away from inspecting. Perhaps you are afraid of damaging them in some way. You need not be, however, as really they need very little care. Clean them each day with a soft sponge and tepid water and ensure that you dry the skin around them afterwards. To prevent unnecessary irritation, do not shake up the bed while a horse is in the stable; also, feed hay from the floor if possible, to prevent seeds and dust from getting into your horse's eyes. In the summer a fly fringe and an effective fly repellent will help to prevent much of the irritation from flies.

One of the biggest problems with the eyes is that they are rather prominent on each side of the horse's head. This means that they tend to get knocked, or foreign bodies enter the eye, which often leads to infection. If something does enter the eye, you will need to take action to prevent further suffering. First, gently remove the offending object, either by picking it out carefully if it

Sharp teeth should be seen to immediately. Most horses need their teeth rasping at least once a year.

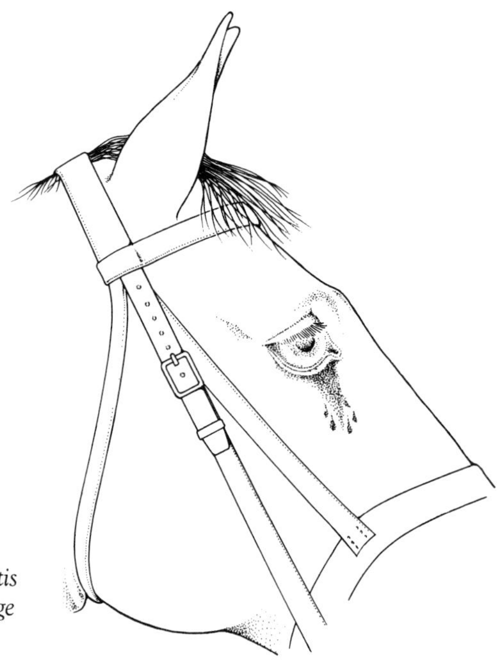

A horse with conjunctivitis will have a tacky discharge leaking from the eye.

is clearly visible or by gently flushing it out with cooled, boiled water. Take *very* great care not to scratch or aggravate the eye surface.

You may find that conjunctivitis follows as a result (this term means inflammation of the conjunctiva – the membrane covering the inside of the eyelids). In such cases you need to give first aid by administering eye ointment or drops. You might find the horse less than enthusiastic, so to ensure best results prepare everything in advance and work in a methodical manner.

The signs which act as a warning of an eye problem are often quite obvious. Check the eyes regularly:

- Is there any discharge?
- Is there any swelling?
- Have the eyelids suffered any injury, however small?
- Does the horse insist on keeping his eyes shut?
- Has the colour of the eye altered – has it become cloudy or dull?
- Does the horse object to bright light?
- Does the horse show any signs of blindness?

If it is not easy to gain access to the horse's eye, ask the vet to attend and in the meantime the horse might find some relief if kept in a darkened area. Do not force the eye open if it is clearly stuck up with discharge or squeezed tightly shut due to pain. In such cases a topical anaesthetic will be needed.

Other conditions that can affect the eye include ulcers, for instance. These usually occur because the cornea (the front part of the eyeball)

To give eyedrops or apply ointment to the eye

1. Ask someone to hold the horse: you may find it impossible on your own.
2. Wash your hands.
3. Ensure that the ointment or drops are at body temperature by standing them in a bowl of warm water for a few minutes, but do *not* overheat. Make sure that the nozzle of the tube or pipette is clean and free from contamination.
4. With some warm, moist cotton wool, wipe away any discharge that may have collected in the corner of the eye.
5. Holding the dropper or tube between your thumb and first two fingers, rest the heel of your hand against the horse's cheek.
6. Gently but swiftly turn out the horse's eyelid with your other hand and immediately squeeze in the drops or apply a line of ointment between eyeball and eyelid. Make every effort not to touch the eyeball with the end of the pipette or tube, as this may cause distress and prevent your horse from co-operating next time.

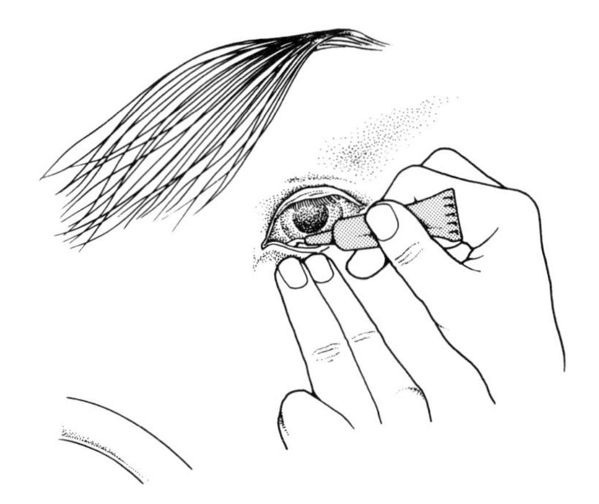

When treating an eye problem, apply the ointment carefully along the inside of the eye-line.

is scratched or becomes infected. Treat them in the same way, with drops or ointment. If you notice such problems as soon as they appear and treat them properly, they will usually clear up quite satisfactorily.

If the response to treatment is not fairly rapid, then call your veterinary surgeon straight away. In any event it is a sensible precaution to alert the surgery to the problem and explain how you are treating it. Be aware that there is a far worse eye condition known as moon blindness, which could cause blindness if not promptly treated by a vet. The danger with this disease is that it shows very similar symptoms to more common ailments.

CHAPTER 3

SIGNS OF ILL HEALTH

Horses that feel off-colour will generally appear listless. They may hang their heads and let their ears droop. They must feel something like we do when all we want to do is to go to bed and sleep it off. You might find that they look 'tucked up', with the tummy pulled in, and might even seem a little unsteady on their feet.

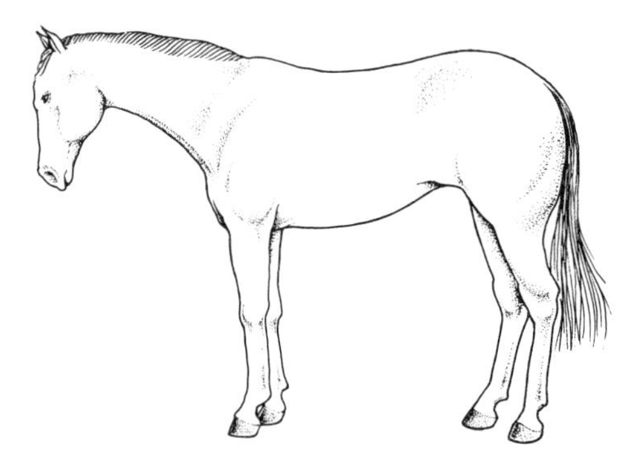

This horse is obviously feeling poorly: he is listless and is hanging his head.

PHYSICAL SIGNS OF ILL HEALTH

A change of colour in the eye membranes

Pale membranes might indicate anaemia, chronic indigestion or worms.

Deep red membranes are a sign of a fever.

Red membranes with a blue tinge indicate pneumonia.

Yellow membranes might indicate a disorder of the liver.

Blue-red membranes are indicative of heart and circulatory problems.

A change in coat

If it is standing on end, or 'staring' and dull in appearance, this is often a good indication of possible malnourishment. If you can pull a horse's mane out easily, this might also indicate ill health.

A change in the skin

Changes in the skin gives several warning signs. Generally the skin of a horse in ill health will tighten up and does not rock freely back and forth as it should. The horse may be in the early stages of a general disease, or may have lice or be generally malnourished. Try the pinch test: does the skin spring back into place?

Signs of sweating

While *excessive sweating* may be caused by too much exercise if a horse is unfit, or by nervousness or excitement, the cause should be evident to you. If, however, a horse

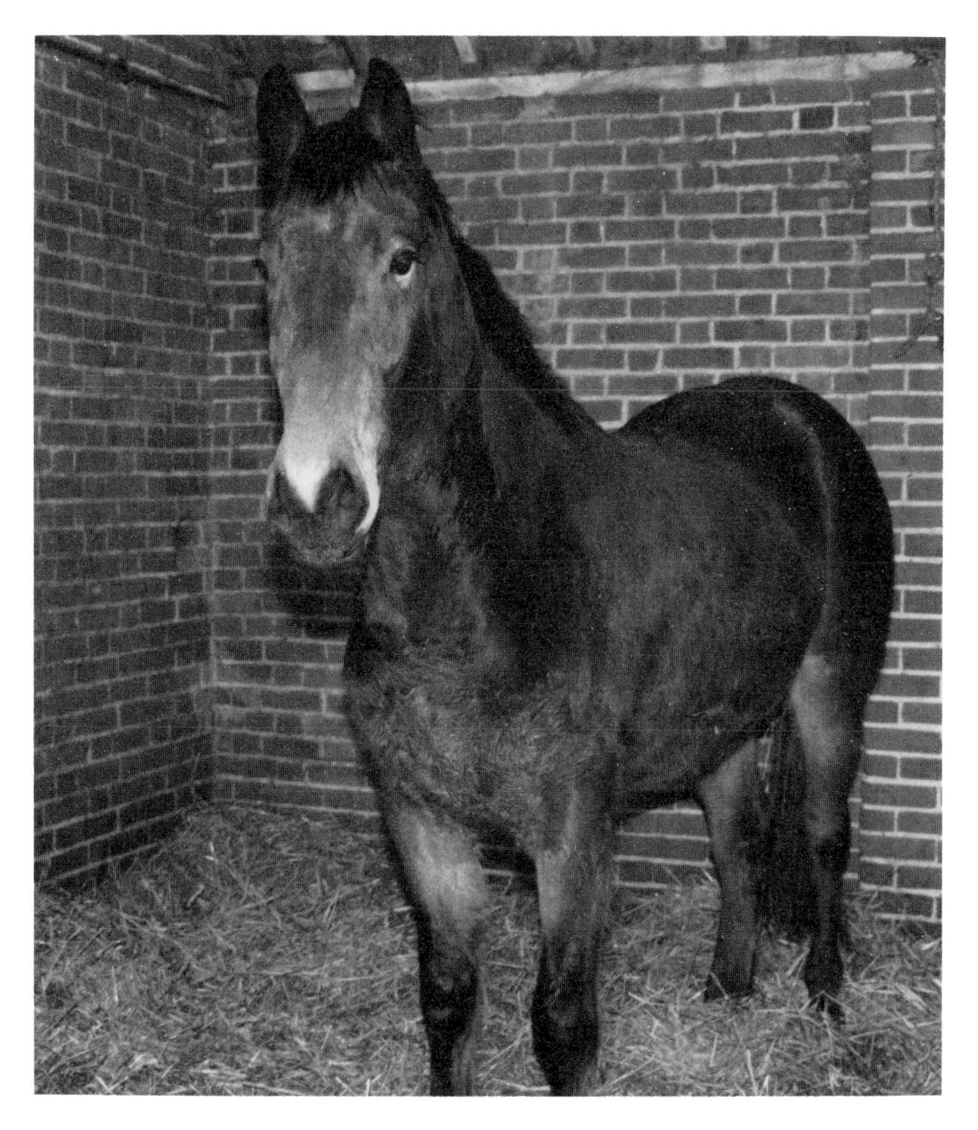

If a horse breaks out into a sudden sweat, investigate further: it could be a sign of illness.

breaks out into a sudden *cold sweat*, it might indicate acute physical pain or some form of mental imbalance. An uncharacteristic *hot sweat* is often a clear indication that your horse has a fever.

Puffy or swollen limbs

Puffy limbs can denote various conditions of ill health. If the puffiness is due to a bone or joint problem, your horse will obviously be lame. If the limbs are generally puffy all over, the problem might be heart trouble or a digestive problem. Localized puffiness may indicate a skin irritation or an injury.

TEMPERATURE, PULSE AND RESPIRATION

You will often see 'TPR' written in books on fitness and in articles in horse magazines. This refers to temperature, pulse and respiration. If your observations lead you to believe that your horse is off-colour, check these three factors. They will either confirm or dispel your suspicions.

Temperature

A horse's normal temperature is 38.0°C (100.5°F) and a variation ranging from about 38.0–38.2°C (100.4–100.8°F) is still normal. Always call your vet if a horse's temperature rises above 38.6°C (101.5°F) or falls below 37.8°C (100°F).

Taking the pulse

Feel under the horse's lower jaw (the bit that comes round in a semi-circle) until you come to the softness of an artery. This one is known as the maxillary artery and is usually the easiest from which to record the pulse. Gently move your fingers along the artery until you come to the place where it crosses the jaw bone. Here you should be able to feel a definite beat.

If a horse is generally fit and well, the pulse rate at rest will be in the region of 35 to 40 beats per minute. If this rate exceeds 50 beats at rest, you need to investigate further as the horse may be coming down with a fever or colic, or may be in pain.

Taking the temperature

1. First, shake the mercury of the thermometer down so that it is well below normal.
2. Lubricate the bulb of the thermometer with petroleum jelly.
3. Lift the horse's tail and, standing to the side, insert the bulb of the thermometer into the horse's rectum at a slight angle. Ease it in, to about half its length, ensuring that you keep hold of the other end. As a safety precaution, securely fix one end of a piece of string to the free end of the thermometer and the other to a peg which is then clipped on to the horse's tail. Then, should you accidentally let go of the thermometer, you will be able to retrieve it and avoid a serious problem.

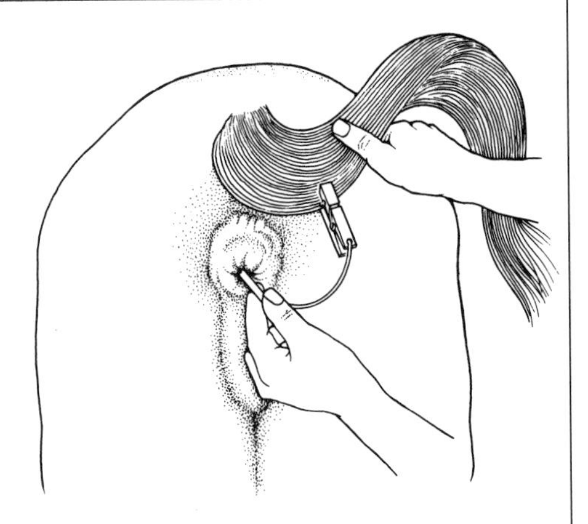

Taking a horse's temperature.

4. After at least one minute, remove the thermometer and read it immediately, wiping it clean first if necessary.
5. Disinfect the thermometer immediately after use to prevent any spread of infection.

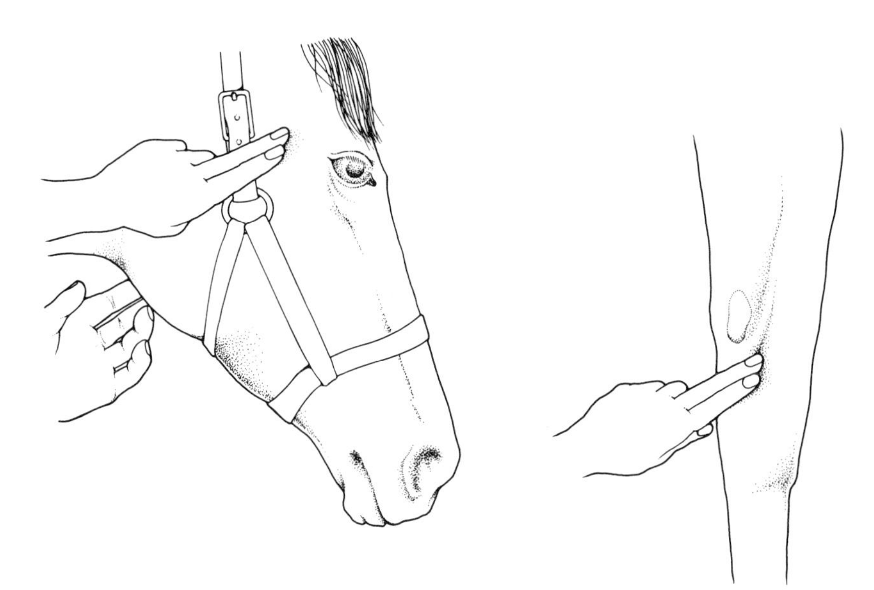

Points at which the pulse can be taken.

Taking the respiration rate

The respiration rate is the number of breaths (counting in plus out as one breath) per minute. This is simply checked by placing a hand over one of the horse's nostrils and then just counting the breaths that you can feel within a minute, or by watching or feeling the movements of the horse's rib cage. While at rest the breaths should be even and regular and the respiration rate of a normal adult horse is between 8 and 12 breaths per minute, depending on the size of the horse: a Shire, for example, breathes at the lower rate (8) and a Shetland pony at the higher rate (12).

PROBLEMS RELATING TO THE GRASS-KEPT HORSE

It is usually more convenient and cost effective to keep your horse out at grass but there are some risks. First you have to consider the type of horse you have. A native breed might not come to any harm in cold weather but a finer, more thoroughbred breed will probably need more protection. To keep horses at grass healthy you must provide them with a shelter, clean water and adequate grass, which may need supplementing with hay in winter. To prevent injuries, ensure that they are enclosed by safe fencing and that they are not subjected to bullying from more dominant horses. It is vital that horses which live out are checked twice a day to see that they are quite well and happy.

To prevent illness you should ensure that the field is free from poisonous plants (Chapter 8) and pesticides. Horses which live out also need to be protected from certain environmental conditions or they will develop diseases such as mud fever or sweet itch.

PROBLEMS RELATING TO THE STABLED HORSE

The horse which is stabled also suffers from the environment, especially if stabled too much. A horse that is stabled for most of the day is more likely to suffer from allergies to hay and stable dust than the horse which lives out. More stabled horses also suffer from colic (Chapter 8) than grass-kept ones. Horses out at grass can exercise themelves but those that are stabled simply have to stand still for most of the time. This can cause problems with your horse's circulatory system, resulting in conditions such as filled legs, azoturia and lymphangitis.

Stabling horses for too long can also cause mental problems. Quite often, the more they are kept in, the more frisky they become when they are ridden – they need to let off steam. Left to their own devices, horses are animals that move about all day. It is unnatural to shut them in a stable with perhaps only an hour's exercise and this is one of the reasons why so many stabled horses develop vices such as weaving and crib-biting.

How are horses best kept, then, if they suffer both when stabled and at grass? It is a matter of a compromise. You need to devise a system that will allow the horse as much freedom in the field as possible, but with some time in the stables for protection from the elements and so that you can ride and care for your horse properly. In the winter, horses are best stabled at night to ensure that they are warm and well fed, while in the summer they are best stabled in the day to protect them from the heat and flies. With a little juggling about you will soon develop a seasonal routine that will best suit you and your horse's health.

WHEN TO CALL THE VET

When you administer first aid, even for the most minor problems, you undertake certain responsibilities. You must first of all assess the condition of the horse and identify the main problem. Even if a problem may seem obvious, it is wise to double check. You then need to decide quickly the most immediate and appropriate form of treatment, administer it and then, depending on circumstances, arrange for a veterinary surgeon to attend.

You should certainly call the vet in the following circumstances:

- When there is an obvious reason for doing so, such as colic or lameness.
- If your horse deviates from normal behaviour and you cannot understand why (you have not changed the feed or exercise, for example).
- If you need the vet to back up your first aid – perhaps to stitch a wound.
- If your horse is due to receive vaccinations or other general health maintenance checks, such as teeth-rasping.
- If you are in doubt about whether or not your horse needs veterinary attention. The vet may be able to put your mind at rest on the telephone, or may make the

decision to come out. In such cases it is far better to be over-cautious.

You can help the vet by keeping a clear record of what you found and what you have done, so that this can be taken into account when further treatment is considered.

SICK NURSING

A sick horse needs to be kept warm and dry, and should be brought in and rugged up to maintain a normal body temperature if necessary. The vet will find it most helpful if you can report what your horse's temperature is when you telephone. Horses suffering from shock particularly need to be kept warm and you may need to use artificial heaters, preferably infra-red. Keep the bedding well banked up, dry and clean, but do not shake it up while the horse is still in the stable as this may cause coughing.

A sick horse with no appetite should be tempted with succulents such as carrots, or by adding sugar beet or molasses to the feed. Electrolytes added to the drinking water will help to maintain essential body salts. As soon as he is able to, you should walk the horse out to provide at least some exercise and turn him out as soon as your vet advises.

To ensure that you do not inadvertently spread any infectious diseases, you should maintain high standards of hygiene. In particular, if your horse has any noticeable discharges, clean them away with disposable materials and clean, tepid water.

Fresh air is essential. Although your horse should be kept warm, do not close the top door of the stable. Ensure that the stable has good air circulation but is free from draughts.

Keep reassessing condition, checking your horse over regularly and taking TPR readings. Inform your veterinary surgeon if there is any change in the horse's condition.

CHAPTER 4

FORMS OF TREATMENT

COLD-HOSING

Hosing with cold water is good for initially cleansing a wound and for treating swellings, strains and bruising:

- *To clean a wound*, allow a trickle of water to run down over the affected area.
- *Where inflammation is present*, cold-hosing is particularly useful as the cold water helps to constrict blood vessels.
- *For injuries or strains* to tendons, ligaments or joints, horses will receive great relief from cold-hosing.

The purpose of cold-hosing is to relieve the heat and pain from the injury, which also relieves any swelling. You need to cold-hose for at least 20 minutes three times a day in the early stages after injury. Allow the cold water to run all the way down and around the horse's leg. After hosing, be sure to dry the horse's heels.

Cold-hosing can also be used as a soothing measure after a long ride or competition.

COLD TREATMENT

Cold treatment is simply a way of cooling an area quickly. In an

Cold-hosing.

emergency this can be done by holding a packet of frozen peas against the injured site, until an ice pack can be obtained. Cold treatment is most useful after a knock of some kind, where bruising is likely to occur. In such cases, the sooner the ice pack is applied the quicker the healing will be, as the cold will check the bruising and help it to disperse.

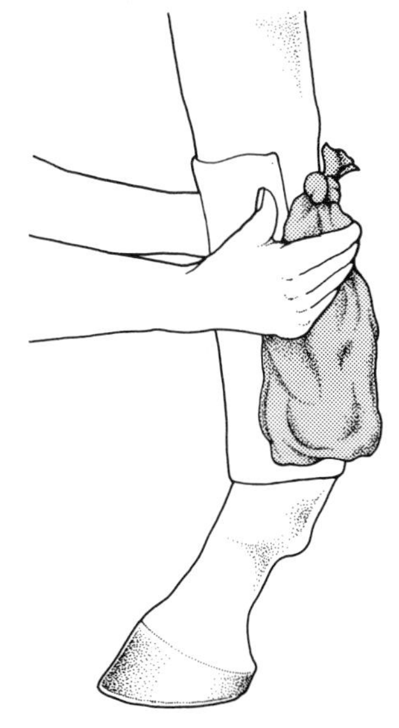

Ice packs.

As a first aid precaution, always have some ice cubes in the freezer. Put these into a plastic bag and crush them with something heavy. Put this into another plastic bag (to prevent melted water from dripping out from holes which might have been made during the crushing stage). Then bandage this over a thin layer of gauze and cotton tissue on the horse's leg. Remove once the ice is melted and re-apply three times daily until the bruising or swelling is healing well.

Specially made, reusable ice packs are available that can be frozen until required and then re-frozen after use. They are very convenient and do save a lot of messing about with crushed ice. There are also some instant cold packs which do not need freezing at all: you simply hit them to split the inside pouch, which releases a cold substance ready for use. Cold compression wrap is also very effective – it is specially designed to absorb moisture, but is still flexible when frozen, which makes bandaging on to a leg very simple.

HOT FOMENTATION

Hot fomentation is useful when trying to reduce inflammation, to extract poison from an affected area, or to bring an abscess to the head so that it can be lanced or until it 'pops' on its own.

Hot fomentation is simply the process of applying heat to an affected area. This can be done by heating a poultice or dressing, which is then applied and perhaps bandaged on, or by placing the affected part (a hoof, for example) directly into hot water – known as **hot tubbing.** The water must not be so hot that it will scald, but hot enough so that you can just bear your hand in it.

Hot poulticing

Where additional power is required to help draw fluids from sprains or wounds, a poultice with special chemicals already impregnated into the dressing can be applied. The type which has a polythene backing attached to help draw fluids, is the type used almost universally now and is very convenient to apply.

Applying a poultice

1. Cut the poultice to the size you will need to cover the injury and place this on a plate. Pour on boiled water which has cooled to about 38°C (100°F).
2. Remove any excess water by placing another clean plate on top and squeezing.
3. Apply the poultice to the site of injury, making sure that the polythene backing faces outwards.
4. Cover with a layer of gauze and cotton tissue and bandage in place, keeping an even thickness all the way around the leg.
5. Leave in place for eight hours.
6. Remove, and apply a fresh poultice. Keep the old poultice to show the vet what has been extracted, if necessary.
7. If no real improvement is seen within 48 hours, it is time to discuss further action with your vet.

   Poulticing the foot is slightly different and is dealt with in Chapter 6.

Blistering and firing

These two traditional methods were commonly used to treat tendon injuries. Their purpose was to increase the blood flow to an area to aid repair, which was achieved (to some degree) as they acted as a counter-irritant around the site of the injury. Firing involved applying hot iron rods to the affected area but it is no longer used, especially as physiotherapy machines provide a better alternative.

Blistering is still used, however, usually to reduce swelling or promote hoof growth. You can apply a mild blister yourself and may even have done so without knowing it, if you bought a preparation for a sprained tendon: a blister is an ointment rubbed into the skin to produce heat.

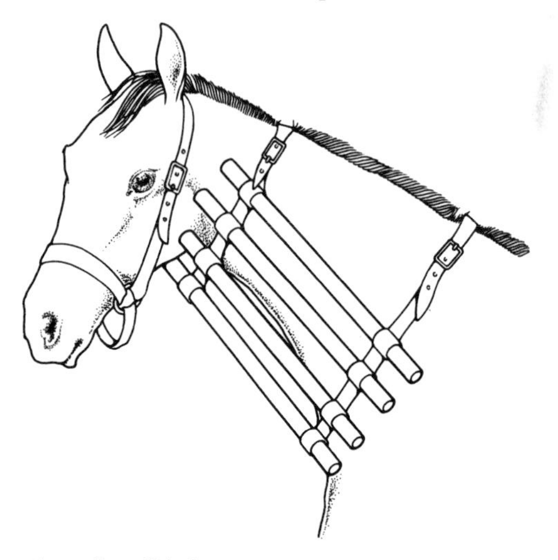

A cradle will help to prevent a horse getting at bandages or touching a blister applied to the legs.

However, you should only contemplate the use of a stronger blister if it is supplied by a veterinary surgeon. If you do use a blister, wear rubber gloves and use a 'cradle' to stop the horse from licking or tearing at the bandage.

ALTERNATING HOT AND COLD TREATMENTS

This is useful for stimulating the circulation, especially where a horse has sprained a limb. Directly after the strain has occurred, use cold treatments for a day. Then begin hot and cold treatments on the second day. Use a hot treatment (such as a hot pad or hot tubbing) on the area

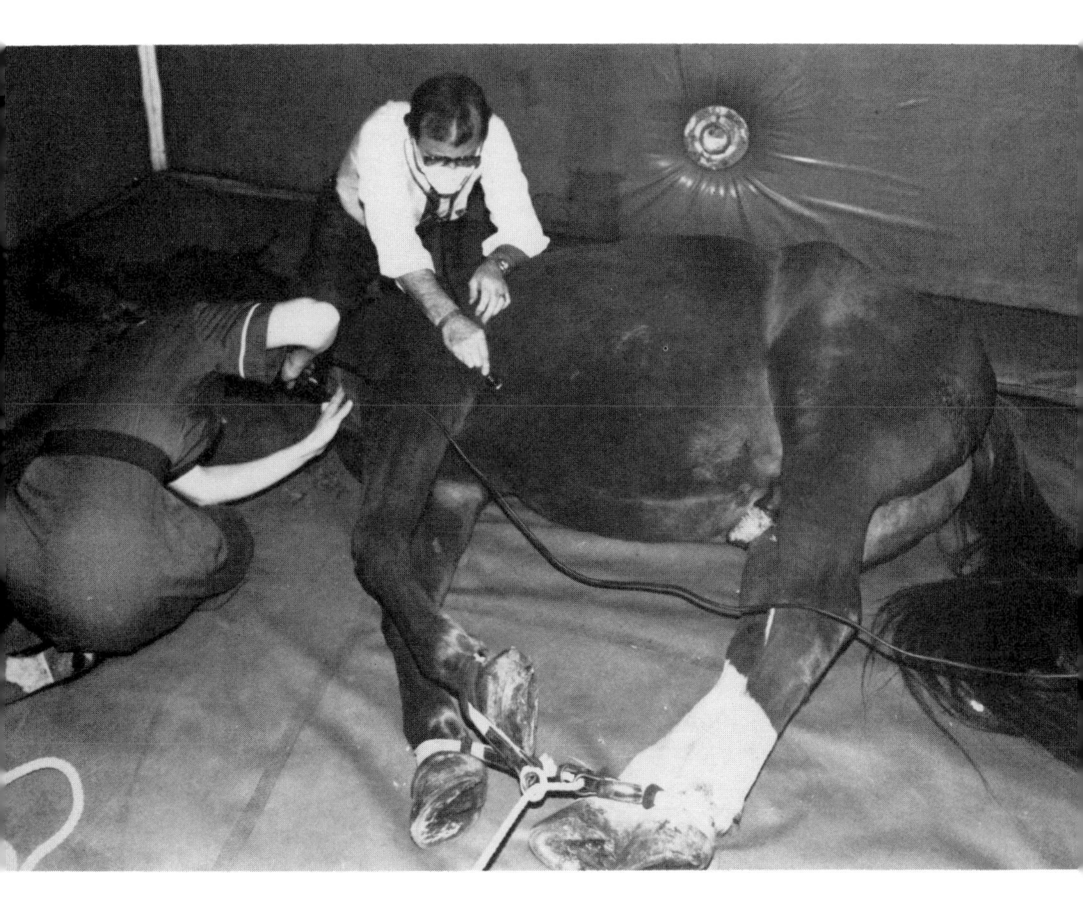

Surgery – the most drastic form of treatment.

for four minutes, followed by a cold treatment (such as a cold bandage or cold tubbing) for the next four minutes; then repeat so that the overall treatment time runs to about 16 minutes.

Do this three times a day, for as long as necessary, until the swelling reduces or until the horse goes sound, for example.

ALTERNATIVE THERAPIES

If an injury is only slight, you can probably deal with it yourself using one of the above methods. However, if it is quite severe or does not progress well, then you should not hesitate to call your veterinary surgeon. Remember – correct early treatment leads to quicker healing.

Sometimes a veterinary surgeon, with your agreement, might decide to involve a physiotherapist or complementary specialist, if deeper tissue damage has occurred. A physiotherapist has the skills and equipment to provide a better quality of healing in some cases than conventional medicine. After the problem has been diagnosed by the vet, the physiotherapist will decide which treatment is most appropriate for the condition.

Ultrasound is useful for joint and tendon injuries, to reduce swelling and alleviate inflammation.

Laser can penetrate deeper into the tissues than conventional treatments and helps to alleviate deep-seated inflammation.

Magnetic field helps to repair and remodel the injured site by employing the electrical properties of the body, using either a pulsed or a continuous magnetic field.

Massage can help to relieve stress and strain to damaged muscles and generally relax a horse.

Other forms of treatment can be given by a complementary therapist:

Manipulation, often referred to as back treatment, is where an osteopath or chiropractor tries to correct problem areas within the musculoskeletal system.

Acupuncture is usually the insertion of needles into specific points of the body to produce physiological responses which enable a self-healing process to take effect.

Herbal remedies use plants that are either fed or applied to a horse for nutritional or healing reasons.

Homoeopathy employs substances, capable of causing disease in a healthy horse, given in minute doses to stimulate the body's own defences.

SURGERY

A very ill horse may need life-saving surgery. This can be very traumatic, but your vet would not advise it

Intramuscular injections

To give the injection work through the following procedure methodically. You will find it quite easy and quick. The first three steps are preparatory:

1. Always ensure that the injection site is free from mud or dirt and is not wet. Wash your hands and swab the site with surgical or methylated spirits.
2. Check that you have picked up the right drug and read the instructions on the bottle carefully, noting the expiry date and batch number. Shake the bottle vigorously. Swab the rubber bottle stopper with surgical or methylated spirits. Unpack a sterile needle and place it on a sterile syringe. At this stage the needle cover is still on. Remove the cover, hold the drug bottle upside down and insert the needle through the rubber into the fluid. Hold the syringe tight with the thumb and forefinger and withdraw the plunger until the syringe is filled with slightly more of the drug than is required.
3. Pull the needle out of the bottle. Keeping it upright, tap the syringe to encourage any tiny air bubbles to rise. To ensure that there is no air in the syringe, push the plunger until a few drips of the drug flow down the needle.
4. Take hold of the small plastic base of the needle and extract it from the syringe. Hold it

between your thumb and first two fingers. Tap the horse firmly with the base of your fist close to the sterile injection site. This prepares the horse for the injection so that he does not suddenly jump when the needle is inserted.

5. The moment of actually inserting the needle is when many horse owners clam up. If this happens to you, stay calm and endeavour to count to three, telling yourself that you are going to put the needle in on three. Insert the needle purposefully, so that it goes in up to the plastic base. Ensure that no blood seeps from the needle as this indicates that it has hit a blood vessel. If this does happen, extract the needle quickly and re-insert in a slightly different position.
6. Attach the drug-filled syringe to the needle and pull back the plunger slightly to ensure that no blood enters the syringe. Start to push the plunger in slowly to administer the drug. Sometimes you may need to push quite hard (this depends on the density of the fluid being injected) and it is a sensible precaution to hold the point at which the needle and syringe join as they can be forced apart if the fluid is particularly thick.
7. Using a steady pressure, keep pushing the plunger in until all the fluid has gone. Do not be alarmed if there is a slight bump at the injection site.
8. Withdraw the needle quickly and purposefully. You may see a few drops of blood appear but this is nothing to worry about. Do not pat the horse strongly on the injection site, but some horses do seem to find a gentle rub with the base of the fist soothing.

The best place to give an injection into the muscle.

When giving an injection, hold the joint where the syringe meets the needle hub, to prevent it from bursting apart under pressure.

unless it was absolutely necessary or if the horse did not have a good chance of recovery. The need for horse operations is fairly rare, however, so do not worry unduly if your horse becomes ill.

GIVING MEDICINES

Administering injections

If you have never had to give a horse an injection, the possibility of doing so might make you a little apprehensive. You might think that it will always be the veterinary surgeon that gives vaccinations, but what if your horse becomes ill and needs a daily injection? It would be very expensive to call a veterinary surgeon out every day. Would you be able and competent to give the injections yourself? You should at least know how, in case you need to do so in an emergency or for a daily course.

There are three normal ways of giving an injection:

- **Subcutaneous:** the fluid is placed under the skin.
- **Intramuscular:** the fluid is placed into muscle tissue.
- **Intravenous:** the fluid goes directly into the blood stream through a vein.

Injections given by persons other than veterinary surgeons **should only be intramuscular**. You can select various injection sites but the neck is the easiest place if you have never injected a horse before. Measure a hand's breadth up from the base of the neck and aim to insert the needle half way between the underside and the crest.

Always remember to discard used needles and syringes safely, and to store any unused drugs in a safe place, discarding them when they run out of date.

Administering non-injectable drugs

Some drugs can be given in different ways – in the feed for example. This is particularly useful with horses that will not allow you anywhere near them with a needle, as long as they will actually eat the food. Disguise the drug by mixing it in well and placing something in the feed that the horse likes, such as molasses or carrots. Slice the carrots lengthways. Large pieces will encourage the horse to salivate over the food while trying to crunch them up, which makes it all smell and taste 'carrotty'. Other disguises are garlic powder, mint essence or apples.

If a horse that objects to injections also refuses to eat feed with drugs in it, however you try to disguise it, then you can use an oral paste. This is simply squirted into the horse's mouth like a worming paste. Your vet will advise as to what type of administration is most effective, but if your horse is a difficult character the most important thing is getting the drugs into him, however you can!

CHAPTER 5

DEALING WITH MINOR WOUNDS

Whenever a horse's skin is broken, it will bleed. A minor wound will usually stop bleeding within a few minutes, but a more serious wound will need immediate action. The danger of infection exists with any wound, so it is important to ensure your horse has regular tetanus boosters.

WHEN TO CALL THE VET

Whether you call the vet depends on the injury and your own experience. However, **you should always call the vet in the following circumstances:**

- If the wound is spurting blood.
- If the wounds needs stitching (if it is deep and/or more than 2.5cm (1in) long, for example).
- If the wound has any foreign bodies embedded in it such as glass shards.
- If the affected area swells up more than a little.
- If the horse has not been vaccinated against tetanus.
- If joint oil is leaking from the wound.
- If you are worried at all about the injury for any other reason.

IMMEDIATE ACTION

If bright red blood can be seen spurting out of a wound, the horse may have severed an artery, in which case your first priority is to stop the flow of blood. If you can see that the blood is coming from a single artery, apply thumb pressure about 2.5cm (1in) along the artery between the wound and the heart, to arrest the flow. If this does not work, firmly hold a pad of clean material over the wound and again apply pressure. If possible, someone else should call the vet immediately, explaining what is happening. If you have to leave the horse to call the vet yourself, bandage the pad firmly in place and be sure to return without delay. Your only thought at this stage is to stop the blood flow. Continue to apply presssure to the pad. If blood soaks through, *do not* remove the pad for a new one but simply apply another pad over the top. Once the bleeding has slowed, the pad can be bandaged firmly and evenly over the area until the vet arrives or treatment can proceed.

Less serious wounds still need attention and you should practise your bandaging and first aid skills before you ever need to use them.

CLEANING WOUNDS

All wounds, however minor, should be cleaned thoroughly if they are to have the best possible chance of healing quickly and well. Very often the flow of blood itself is enough to clean the wound. If dirt is visible in minor wounds, it can be carefully removed and the wound further

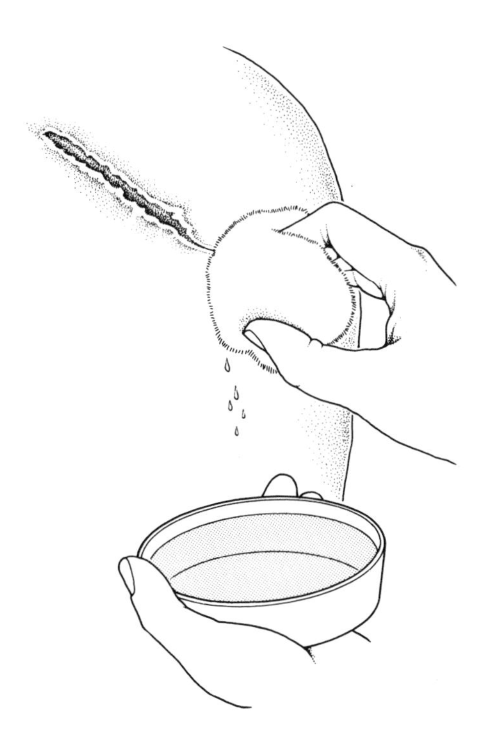

When cleaning a wound, work from the inside outwards, or top to bottom, and frequently change swabs.

cleaned with a swab soaked in warm salty water (about one teaspoon of salt to half a litre or one pint of water). Work from the middle outwards, using a clean swab each time. If dirt is still present it is usually sufficient to run a hose pipe above the area, so that a gentle trickle of water removes any dirt and congealed blood. Do not at this stage use any pressure as this may push dirt further into the wound.

After cleaning, minor cuts should be left to dry and then treated sparingly with an antiseptic powder or spray. This process should be repeated three times daily until the wound has dried up and is mending well. However, if the cleaned wound obviously needs stitching, cover it with a clean piece of gauze and cotton tissue, bandage in place, and call your vet. Do not apply any healing creams, powders, sprays or gels as this will only hinder the vet.

More serious wounds will need dressing and badly infected wounds may need poulticing to draw out dirt and infection (see pp. 35–6). If the wound is not infected, apply a lint wound dressing directly on to the wound, cover with a piece of gauze and cotton tissue and bandage into place over another layer of gauze and cotton tissue which extends all the way down the leg.

BANDAGING

This needs to be done well otherwise it will cause problems of its own. If bandages are put on too loose they will fall off, perhaps causing the horse to trip up. If they are too tight they will interfere with the circulation. Putting on a firm support bandage correctly will help to minimize the swelling from an injury and will offer protection from any accidental external pressure. Taping over the top of the bandage tapes will help to prevent a horse from picking them loose with his teeth.

Bandaging the lower limbs

How to bandage the lower limb.

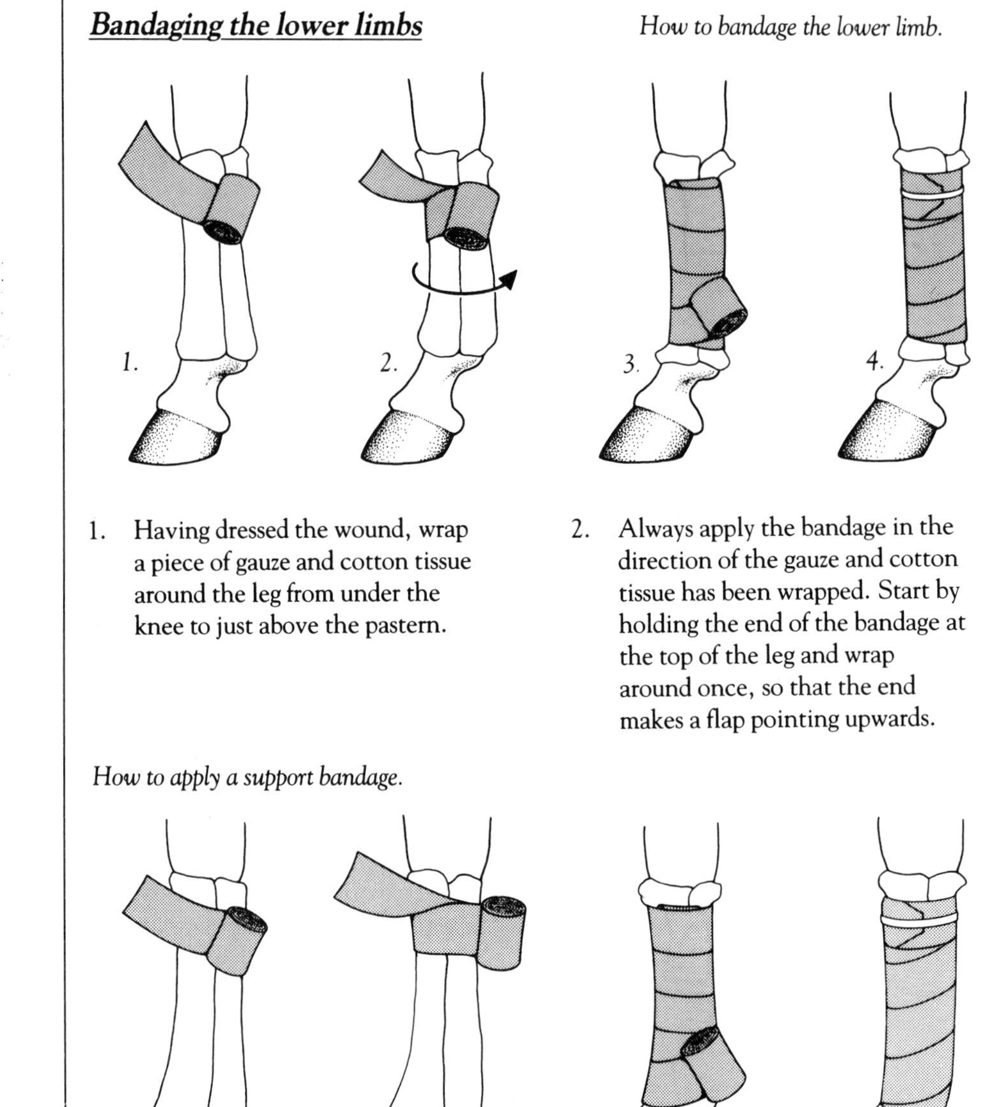

1. Having dressed the wound, wrap a piece of gauze and cotton tissue around the leg from under the knee to just above the pastern.

2. Always apply the bandage in the direction of the gauze and cotton tissue has been wrapped. Start by holding the end of the bandage at the top of the leg and wrap around once, so that the end makes a flap pointing upwards.

How to apply a support bandage.

Bandaging awkward areas

Wounds are often in places where it is more difficult to keep on a bandage. For example, the **forearm** is a common site of injury but it is difficult to keep a dressing in place on it. Start by dressing and bandaging as for the lower limbs but do not go below the top of the knee with the bandage. Make sure that the bandage is not too tight and that the pressure is even all the way down. The biggest

3. Fold the flap down over the first layer of the bandage and continue downwards, covering the flap on the next turn, keeping a firm, even pressure as you go. Do not pull the bandage so tight that there is no 'give' left in it. When you reach the pastern, wrap the bandage around in a criss-cross fashion – it may take a natural turn upward, leaving a shallow 'V' shape at the front – then work back up the leg again.
4. Secure the tapes of the bandage on the outside of the leg and tuck in the loose ends to stop them being accidentally knocked and pulled loose.
5. A stable bandage should then be applied over the top to prevent the horse from tearing at it and to offer added protection from knocks. Use a piece of padding that extends from just below the knee to the coronet.
6. See step 2.
7. Continue bandaging to just above the coronet, then follow step 3.
8. As step 4. It is essential to also put a support bandage on the opposite limb, as your horse will take the weight off the injured leg onto the good one.

problem with bandaging in this area is preventing it from slipping down. A strip of sticking plaster may be required around the upper part of the bandage to prevent any slippage, but ensure that the plaster is no tighter than the bandage itself.

When bandaging **knees and hocks**, use a figure-of-eight technique. Put plenty of padding around the joint, and bandage in place using a slightly elasticated or

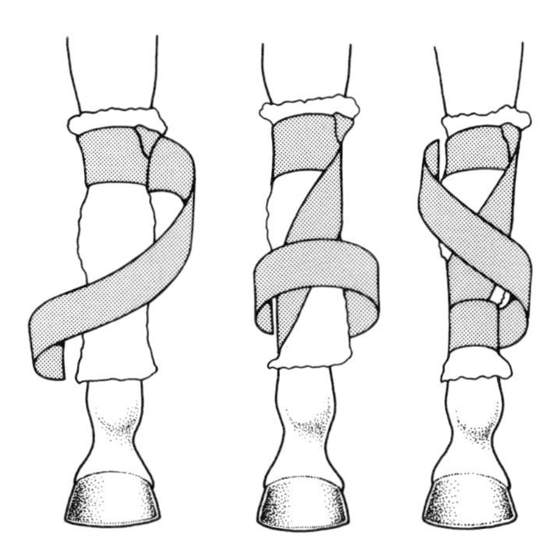

Bandaging a knee.

self-adhesive bandage. When done correctly, a knee bandage forms a cross at the front of the knee but the back of knee is not covered by the bandage, which still allows the joint to bend. When bandaging the hock, do the reverse so that the point of the hock has the cross over it and the front is left uncovered.

Tubular bandage provides an excellent alternative for securing a dressing in areas such as the knee or hock. It is pulled on like a stocking and can simply be folded up whilst changing the dressing and cleaning the wound, and then folded back down again once a clean dressing is in place. To enable movement of the joints a gap can be cut out over prominent bones.

To prevent the bandage slipping, once in place tape around the top.

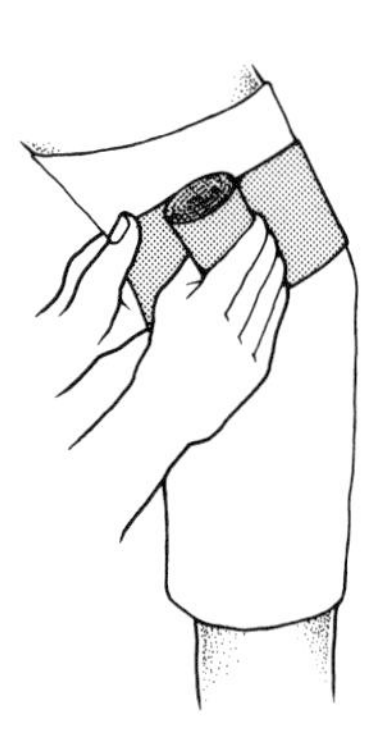
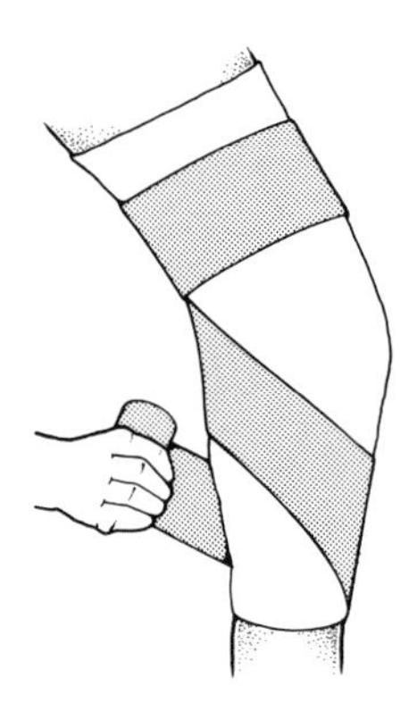
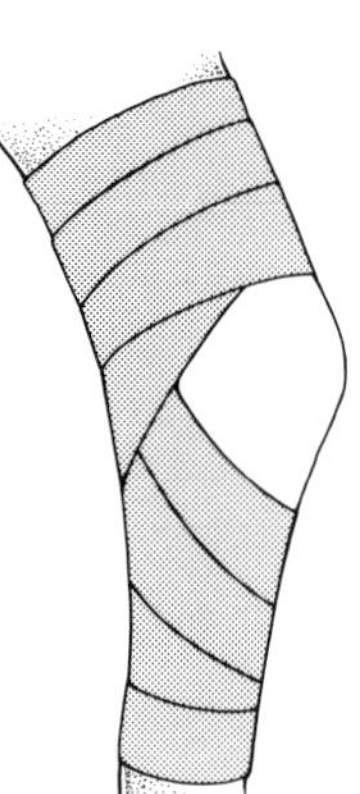

Bandaging a hock.

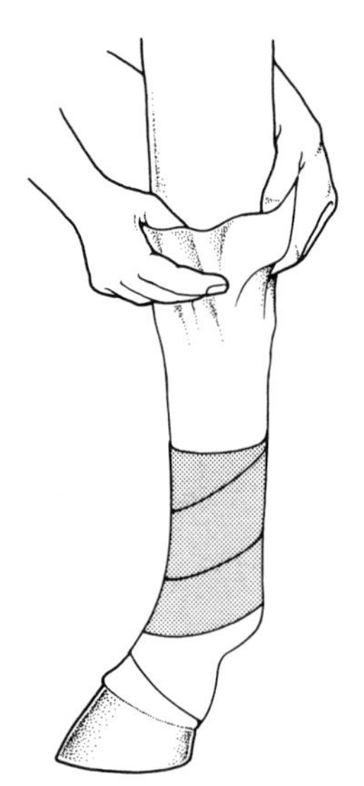
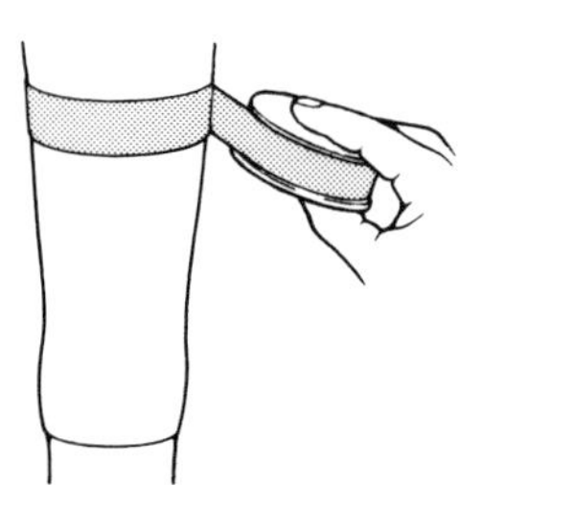
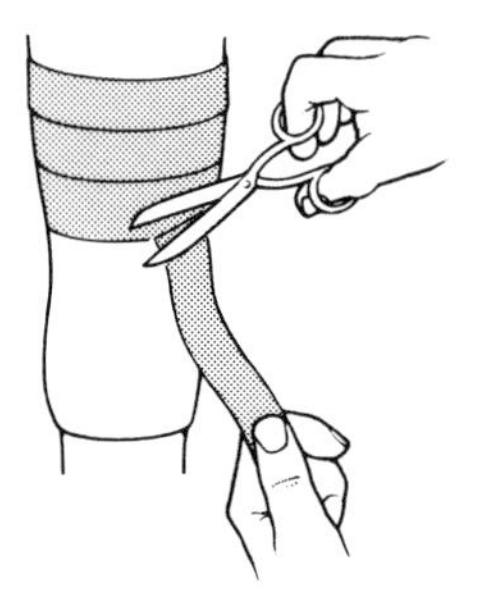

Tubular bandage is excellent for holding a dressing in an awkward place. It can easily be rolled up while the injury is being attended to, and then rolled down again. Tape the bandage into place to prevent it slipping.

SCARRING

Where movement is unavoidable, healing will be delayed and proud flesh will very often occur. Once infection has been overcome, the use of lasers or ultrasound is beneficial in limiting proud flesh formation and can speed up the recovery process considerably, by creating the best conditions for healing to take place.

A poorly managed wound will often reopen and cause excessive scarring, while a wound that has been well cared for will heal more neatly without further complications.

CHAPTER 6

THE FEET

Most horses suffer from a foot-related problem at some time in their lives and reasons for this include:

- Naturally poor feet, which may be inherited – thins walls or dry, brittle horn, for example.
- The feet have been neglected.
- The diet has been neglected.
- The horse has suffered some form of injury or disease.

A clear case of neglect. You should never allow your horse's feet to get into this state.

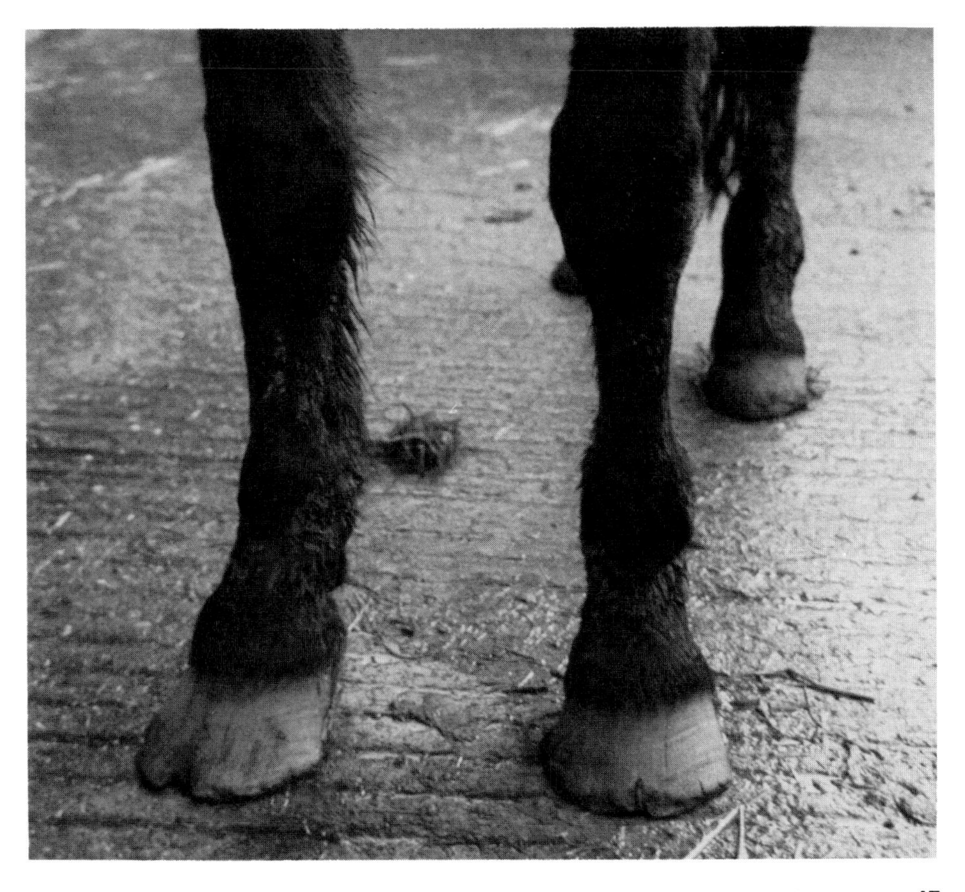

The ideal situation is to buy a horse with good strong feet, but as horses do not come in 'ideal' packages you will probably have to make the best of the natural condition of your horse's feet. The two key rules are:

- Do not neglect your horse's feet in any way.
- Treat any problems which do occur promptly.

'No foot – no horse' is an old saying but it is as true today as it has ever been.

ATTENTION BY THE FARRIER

All horses, whether ridden or not, should be regularly attended to by a farrier. The period between visits varies from horse to horse, depending on hoof condition and growth and whether they are shod or not, but on average a horse needs attention by the farrier every four to six weeks. Your farrier will often spot potential problems and can take immediate preventive action when necessary.

Assessing the healthy foot

- The healthy foot has a strong, hard sole which is neither flaking nor crumbling.
- The frog should be firm and dry.
- When the hoof is on the floor, the frog should come into contact with it.
- The hoof wall should be strong, without cracks or definite ridges.

Such a hoof is likely to cause the least amount of shoeing problems.

PROBLEMS

If you suspect a hoof-related problem, first feel for heat in the foot. Place your hand over the suspect hoof and hold it there until you can feel a constant temperature. Then place the *same* hand over the other hoof to see if there is any difference between the two.

If you do detect heat, have your horse trotted up on a level surface to check for lameness. Ask the handler to leave the horse's head loose: if he is lame in a forefoot, he will lift his head as the affected foot hits the ground; with the hindfeet, he will drop his head as the affected foot touches the ground.

SPLITS AND CRACKS IN THE HOOF WALL

Cracks in the hoof wall are not usually emergencies, but they do need prompt attention if they are not to get worse and cause lameness. Cracks in the hoof wall and dry brittle feet go together and are the major cause of horses casting shoes. There are two main types of cracks: those which start at the ground and work upwards are known as **grass cracks** and those which start at the coronary band and work downwards are known as **sand cracks.**

In the majority of cases the cracks only involve the horn, and as long as they are attended to promptly and correctly the horse should remain

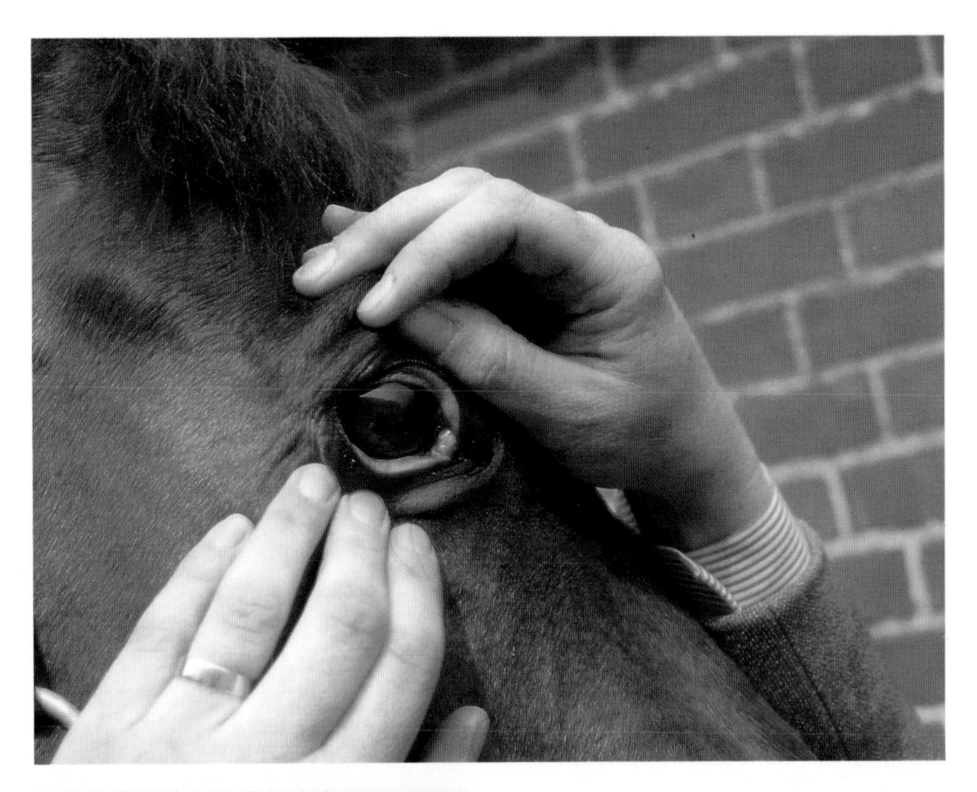

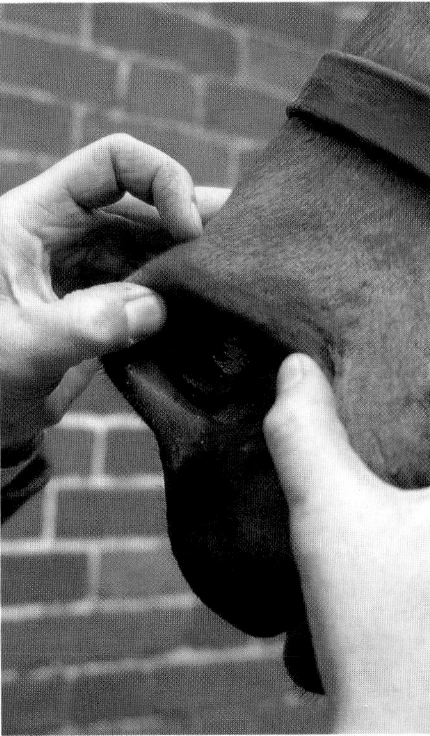

The inside of a healthy horse's eyelids should be a nice salmon-pink.

The nostrils should be moist, and they too should be a nice salmon-pink colour inside.

Estimating body weight. *Top:* measuring the heart girth. *Bottom:* measuring the length from point of buttocks to the point of shoulder.

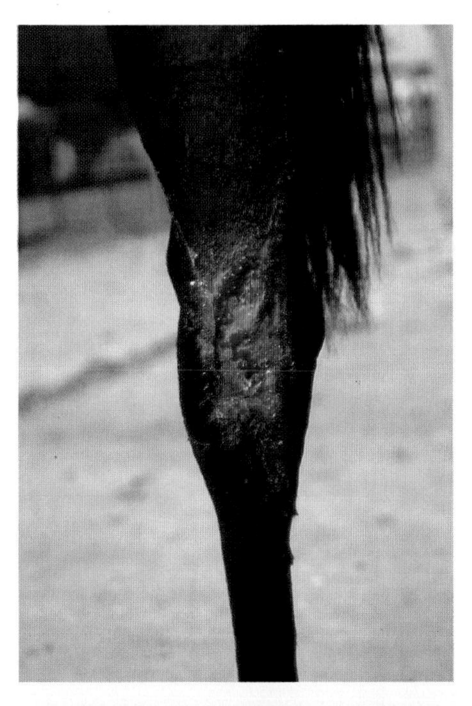

The effects of barbed wire can be all too serious.

The eye should be bright and focused, not listless as seen here.

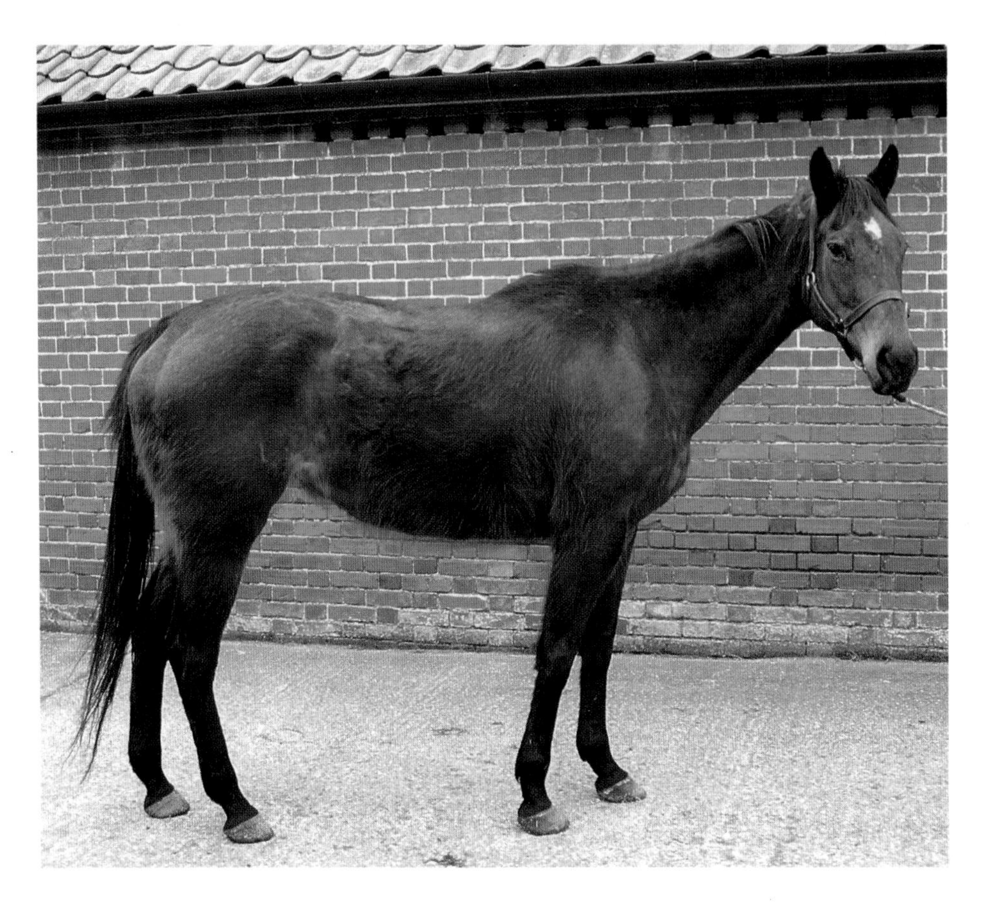

Insufficient feeding has led to malnutrition in this horse and through neglect she is also showing signs of skin disease.

Taking the respiration rate.

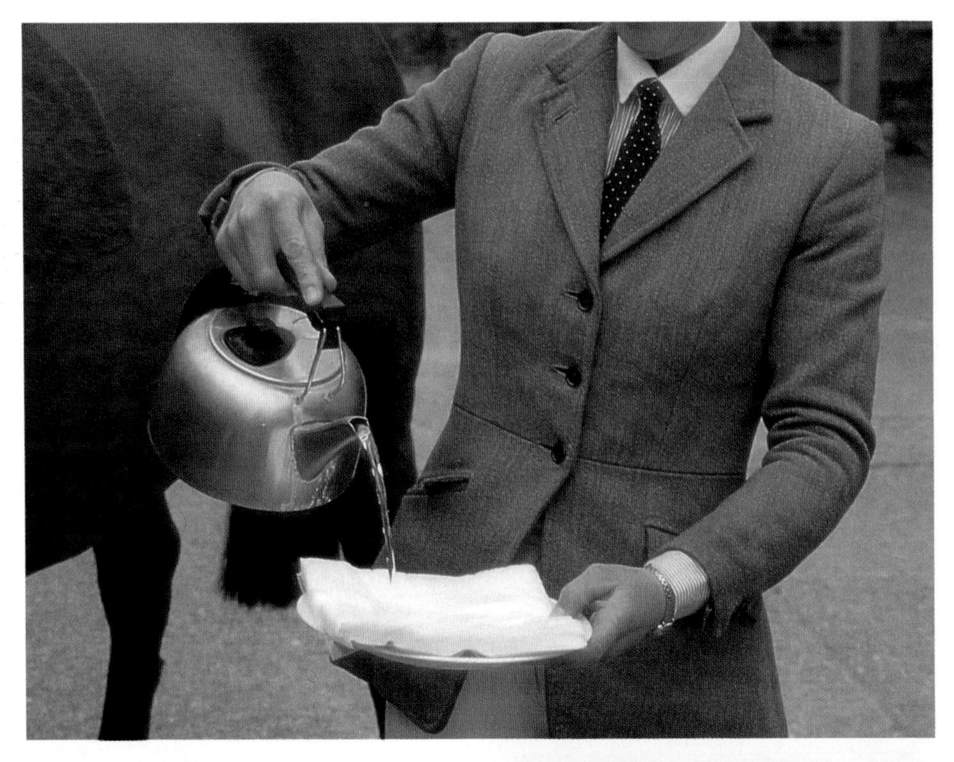

Pour hand-hot boiled water over the poultice.

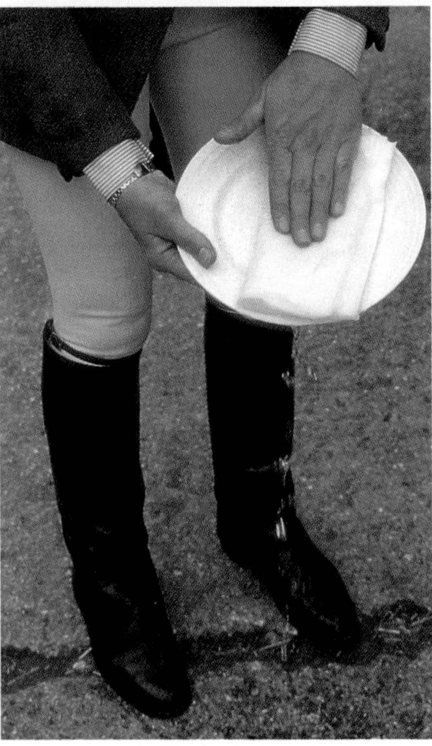

Squeeze out the excess water.

Place the poultice (polythene side outward) over the injury, then cover with a layer of gauze and cotton tissue and bandage in place.

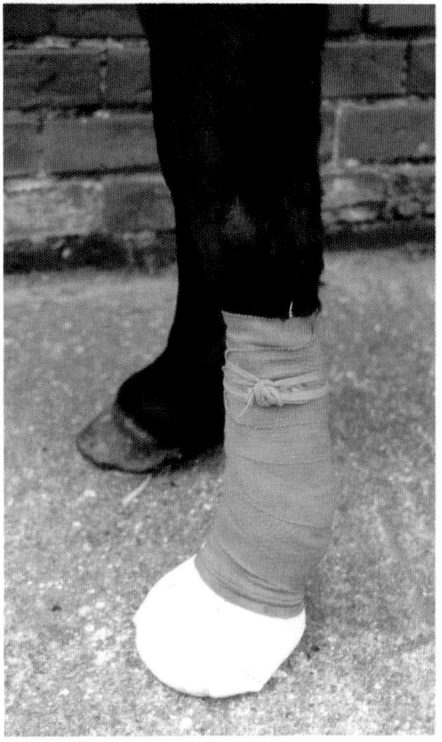

A poulticed foot needs to be secured really well, or it will work loose.

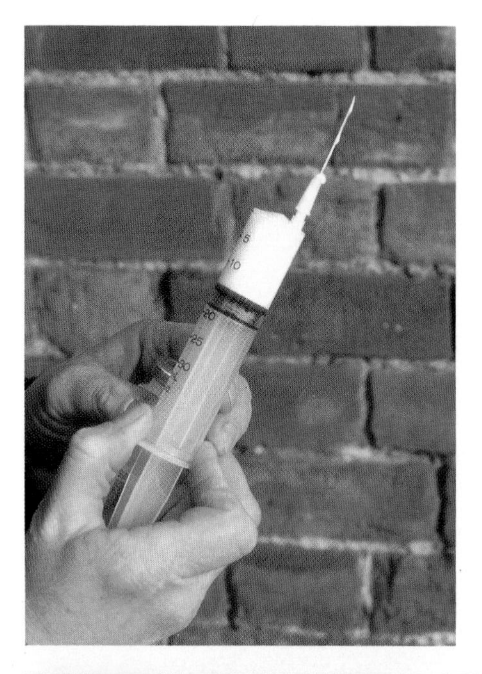

Make sure that all the air is out of the syringe before giving an injection.

Many drugs can also be mixed into the feed. Try to disguise the smell with carrots or molasses.

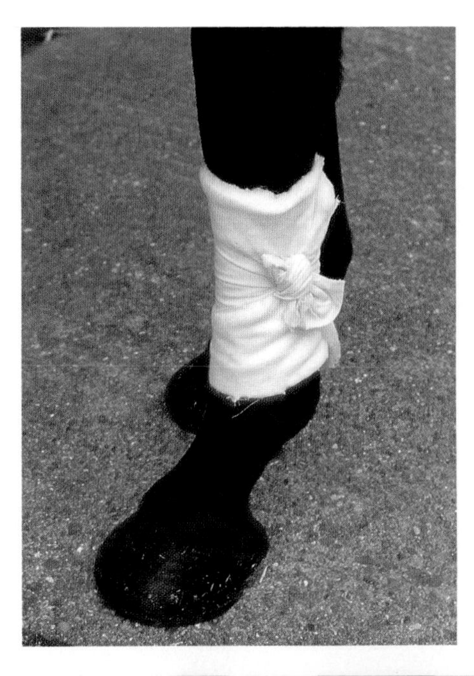

To stop the flow of blood from a wound, place a clean piece of gauze and cotton tissue over it and apply pressure.

Remember to bandage the good leg as well to offer some support.

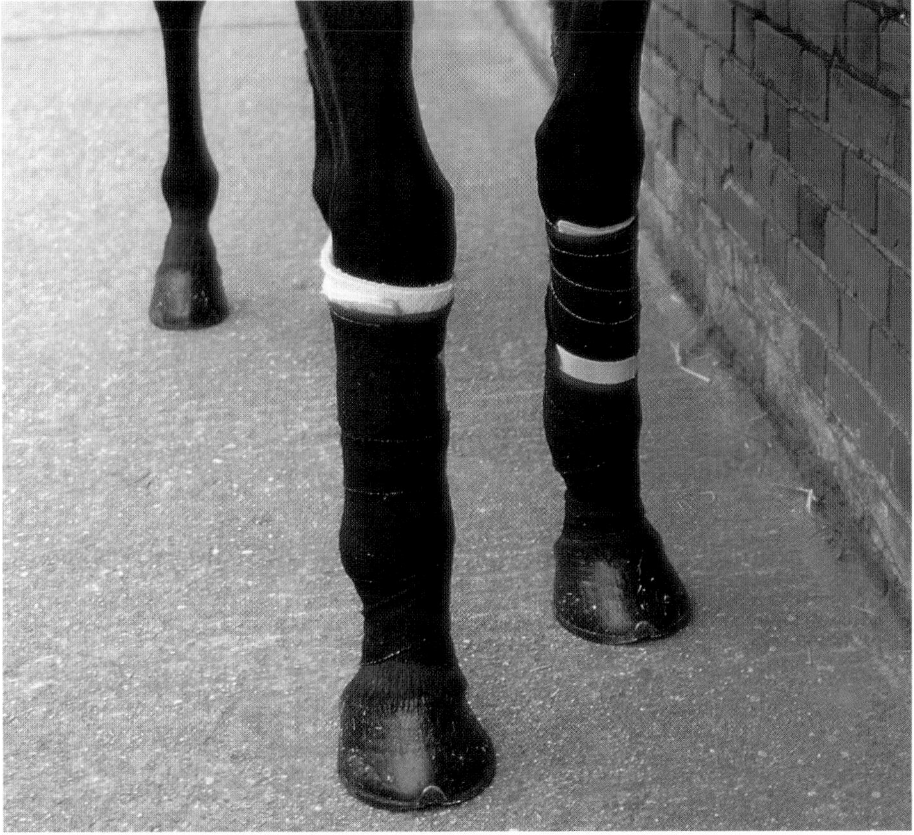

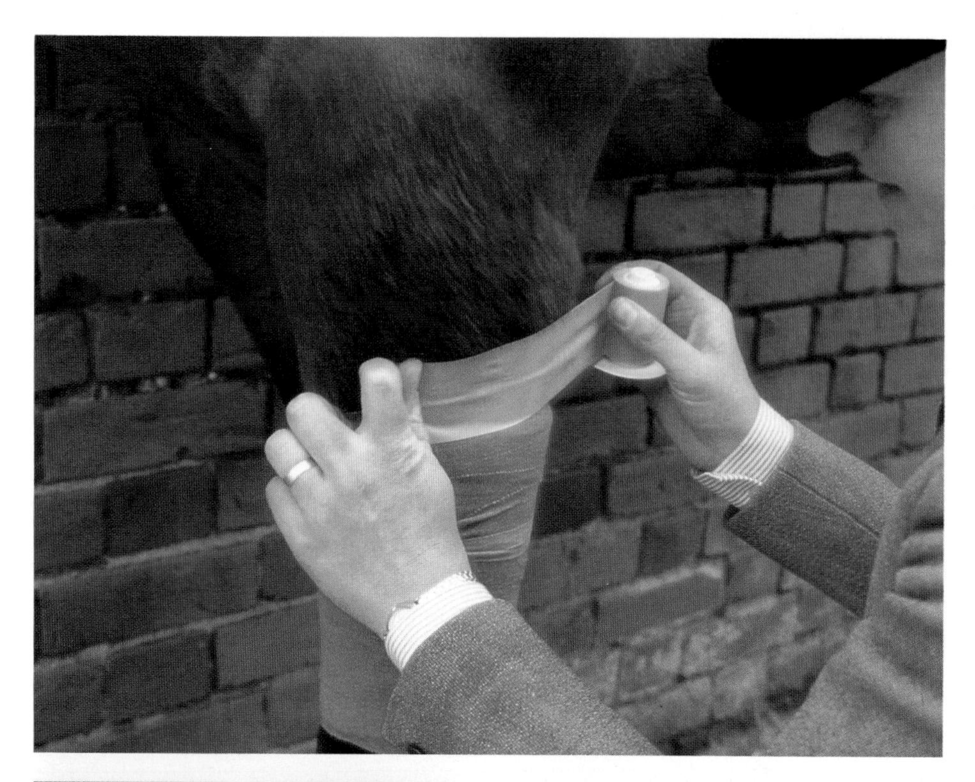

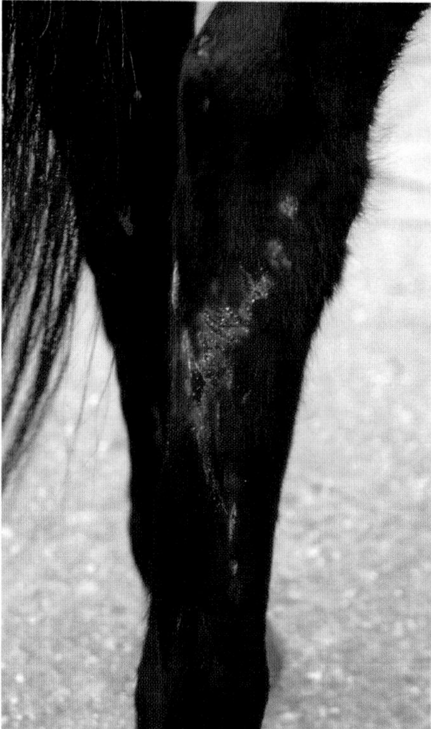

Bandages in awkward places should be taped to secure them.

Scarring is often worse when a wound has been poorly managed.

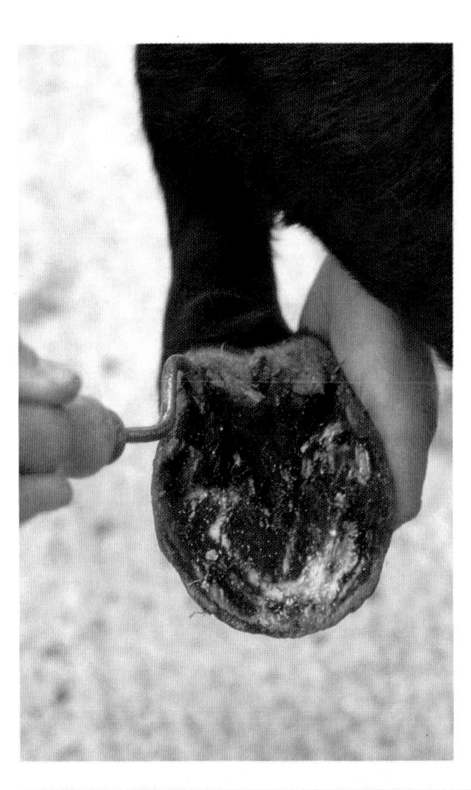

Thrush: the frog appears spongy and wet, and there is a foul-smelling black discharge.

If you find a nail sticking in your horse's foot, remove it immediately to prevent further damage and then treat as a puncture wound.

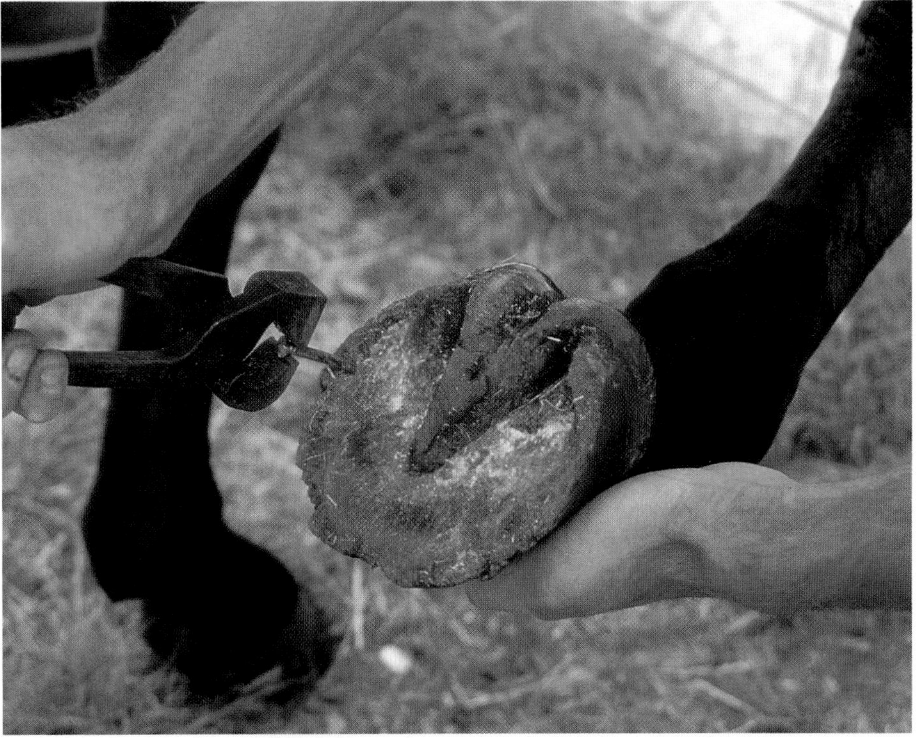

Many horses with colic will get down and roll violently.

Ragwort is one of the most common poisonous pasture plants.

A horse that has colic may frequently attempt to pass urine, but only be able to pass little amounts or none at all.

Horses with COPD develop a nasal discharge which in time turns to a thick yellow consistency.

Bot flies lay their eggs on a horse's leg so that when the horse licks his leg he will take the eggs into his system.

The type of warts commonly seen on a youngster's face.

Girth galls are caused by badly chosen or poorly fitted girths, or by putting a girth on top of mud and sweat.

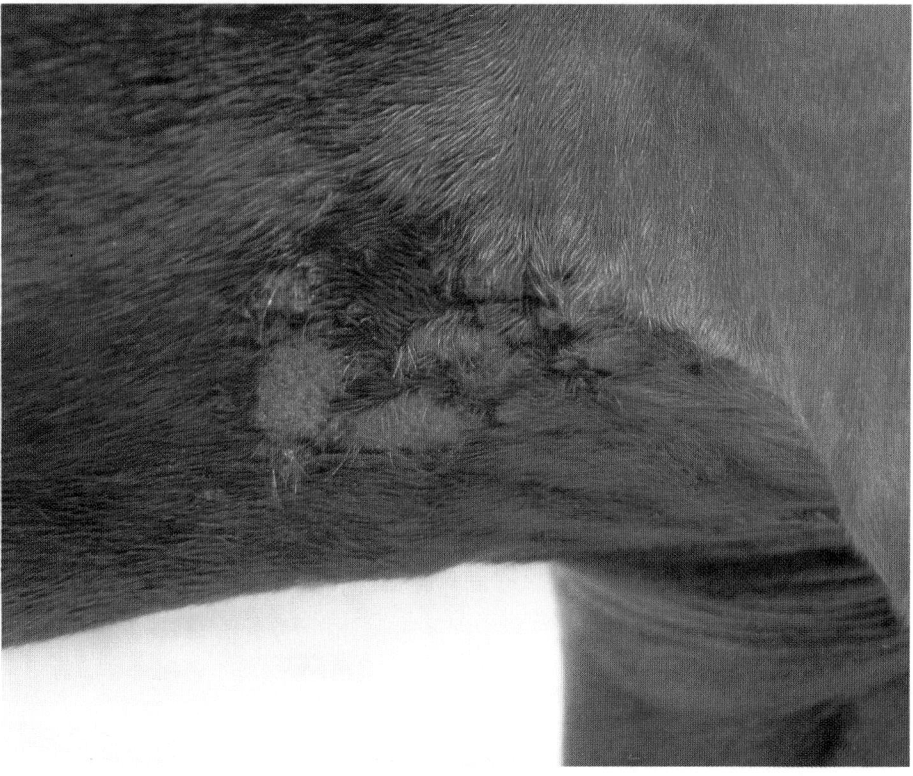

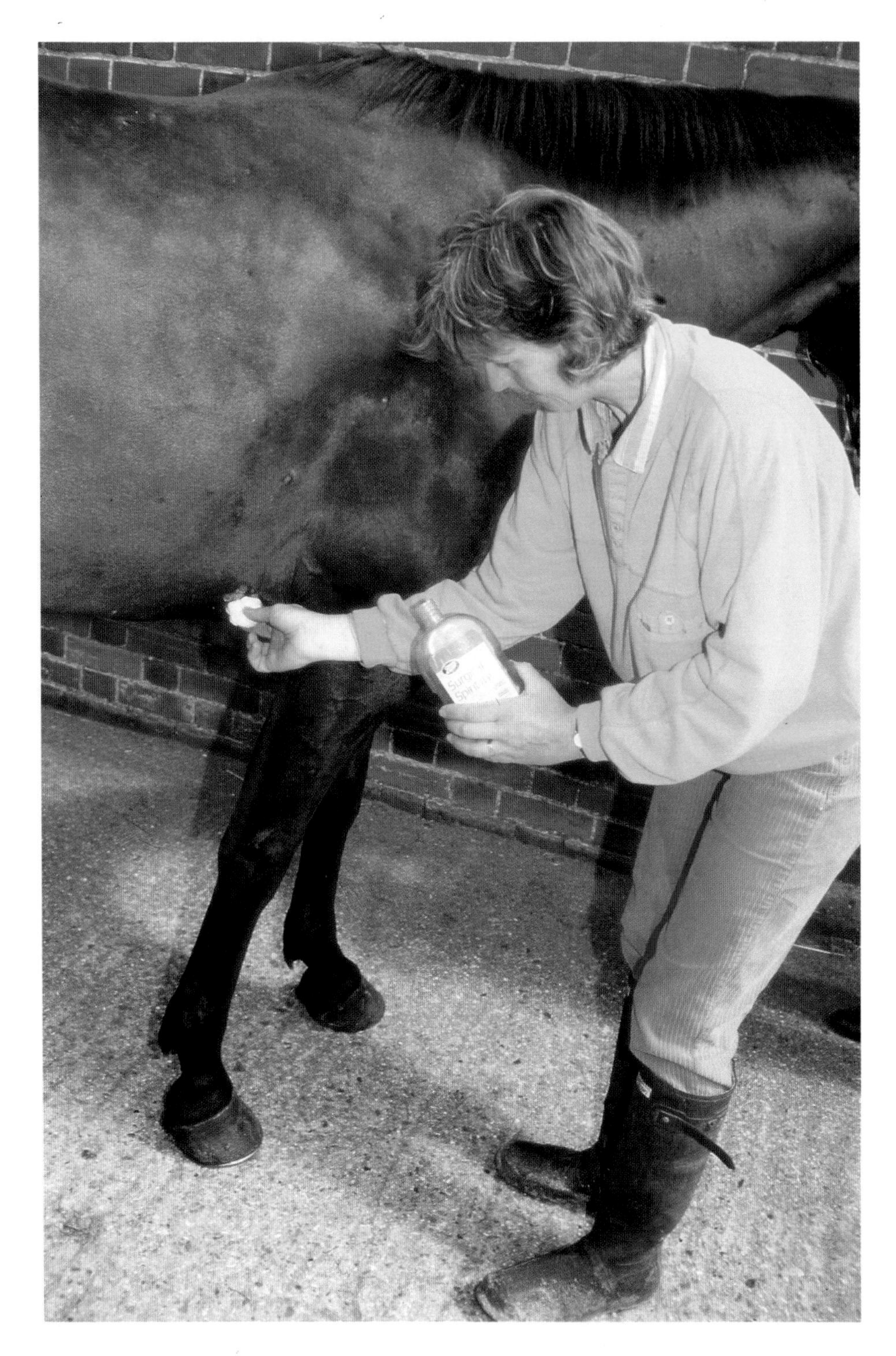

To harden skin in the areas most prone to galling, rub in surgical spirit daily.

To help promote healthy hoof growth in the future there are various measures you can take. However, you will need to be patient as it can take up to a year for a horse to grow a completely new hoof.

- First ensure that the feet are kept well trimmed and that the farrier does a good job. If you are not satisfied or have any particular worries, do not be afraid to air them.
- Feed a good balanced diet.
- If the quality of your horse's feet is poor, supplement the feed with biotin or a multi-compound supplement designed for the job.
- You could apply a hoof dressing designed to strengthen and improve the condition of brittle feet.
- You could apply a product designed to encourage hoof growth.
- In the summer months, try to find a stream in which you can stand your horse for about 15 minutes, or alternatively use a hose if you can spare the time. Wet the hooves for long enough for the water to soak into them. Oil them after they have superficially dried, to prevent the loss of the moisture you have put in. If you oil them without having wetted them, you will be preventing any moisture from getting in at all.
- Avoid riding over hard ground or on the road too much, or in deep mud. But do not stop exercise, as it helps to promote healthy growth.

sound. If a horse goes lame, then it is likely that the crack goes deeper into the sensitive tissues of the hoof, known as the **laminae**, or that they have become infected. Sometimes you may see pus draining out of the hoof, in which case you will need to poultice it (as with a punctured sole, see p. 50) before any corrective action can be taken by your vet or farrier.

The farrier will be able to assist in the healing of a superficial crack by burning a groove at the top of the crack, or using a clip, to stop it travelling any further up or down the hoof.

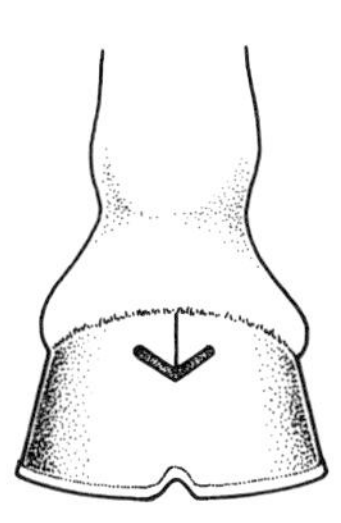

To prevent this hoof crack from travelling any further down, a 'v' has been grooved in.

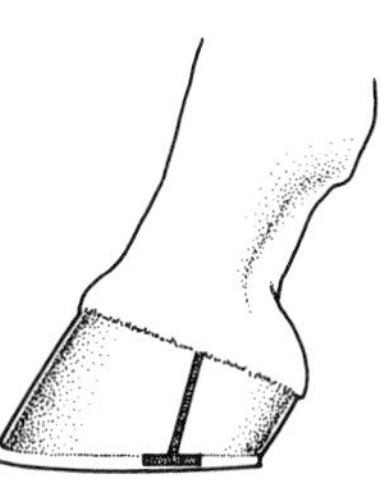

A special shoe will help to heal this type of crack on the side of the hoof.

PUNCTURED SOLES

Puncture wounds to the foot are very common and are often caused by a horse standing on a sharp object, such as a nail or flint. Occasionally, a farrier will drive a nail close to or into the sensitive parts of the foot – this is known as **nail bind** or **pricked foot.**

All puncture wounds should be taken seriously as the wound can heal over and become infected, creating pus that forms a painful abscess. Tetanus is also a risk (especially if tetanus boosters are not up to date). Call your vet for all but the most superficial of such wounds.

Immediate action

You may be alerted to a punctured sole in two ways. A horse may either be hobbling with an offending item still in the hoof, or will suddenly go very lame. If the offending object is still in the foot, remove it immediately, being careful to prevent further damage. Once removed a hole or 'prick' will be clearly visible. To prevent infection this puncture needs to be treated and covered. To clean the affected sole, first wash off any dirt and mud and then dip the foot into a solution of salt water or mild antiseptic to help kill any infection. Keep the area clean by covering it for a few days and check to make sure that no infection is present before turning the horse out again.

If the foot is infected the horse will be lame. There may be no visible sign of anything entering the foot but the vet should be called. In the meantime, poultice the foot; this will help to soften the sole and draw the pus, ready for paring (cutting away). The vet may need to cut a hole in the sole to allow the pus to drain out.

THRUSH

Thrush is a condition that usually results from a horse being allowed to stand on dirty, wet bedding for long periods, especially where the feet are not picked out regularly. The frog appears spongy and wet, and there is a foul-smelling black discharge.

First, clear out the old bedding and keep the stable dry and clean in the future. Clean and scrub the foot out daily; once it is dry, spray on an antiseptic spray. To protect the foot from wet bedding, apply Stockholm tar. Thrush will usually clear up rapidly. However, if the condition has been neglected to such an extent that the sensitive laminae have been affected, then the foot will need to be poulticed (as with a punctured sole, see opposite).

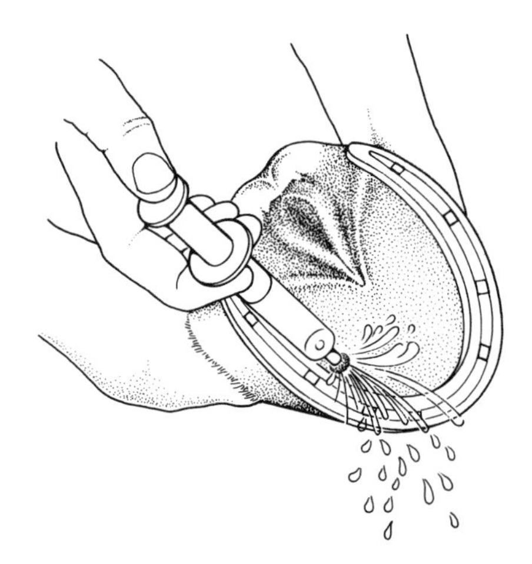

Flushing out a puncture wound in the foot.

Applying a foot poultice

The poultice is prepared in the same way as a poultice for a leg wound. It is then applied to a clean foot that has been previously dipped in a mild antiseptic. Proper securing of the poultice is important and can be quite tricky:

1. Apply the poultice and use a large square of sheeting material or sacking to cover it. This needs to be big enough to travel up around the pastern.
2. Run the bandage around the pastern a few times and then draw it round and over the foot diagonally.

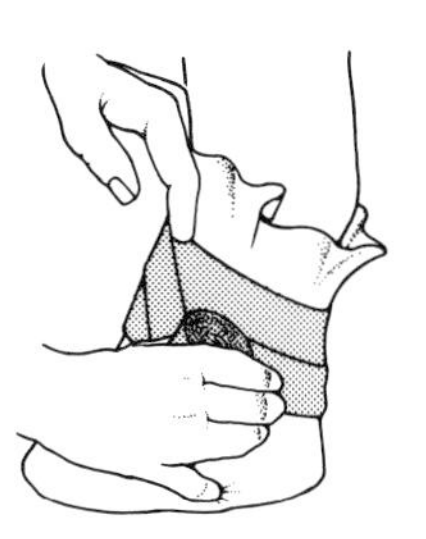

3. Repeat this but run the bandage diagonally in the *other* direction, so that you end up with a cross on the bottom of the foot.

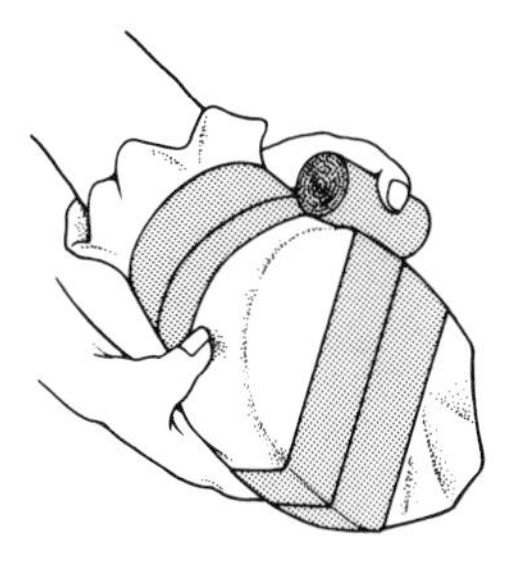

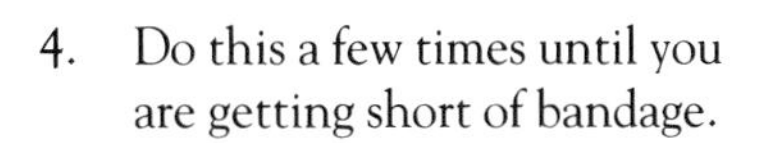

4. Do this a few times until you are getting short of bandage.

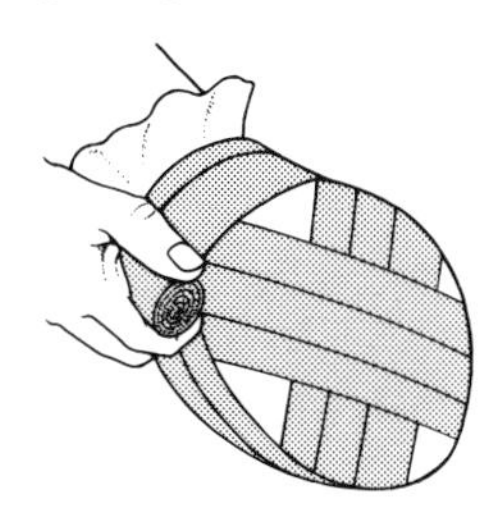

5. Run the bandage back up underneath the pastern and secure it.

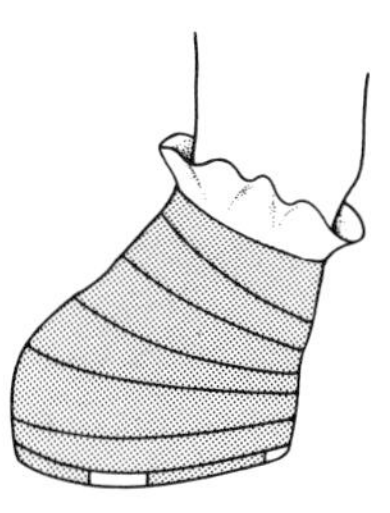

Specially designed boots can be used to keep a poultice on and it is a good idea to have one of these as a stand-by.

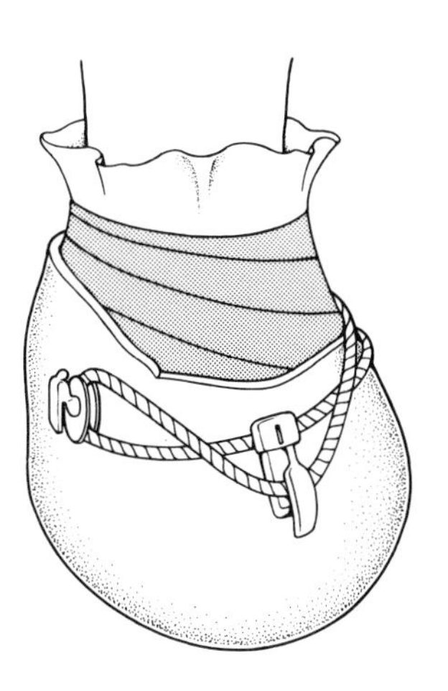

SEEDY TOE

This is a hollow under the wall of the hoof, usually at the toe, where the sensitive laminae separate. The hollow fills up with crumbling horn, which easily comes away on the end of a hoof pick. The condition is thought to have various causes but is often linked to infection or laminitis.

Initially the farrier will need to trim the toes. Then you should scrub out the hollow, pack it with cotton

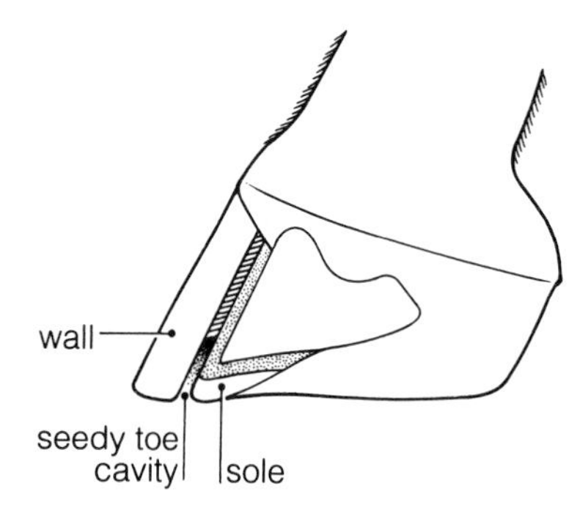

Seedy toe, between the wall of the hoof and the sole.

wool and cover with Stockholm tar. Alternatively ask the farrier to put a leather pad under the shoe to prevent dirt getting into the hollow. Some farriers use a substance which 'sets' into the hollow and provides more stability.

Take measures to promote healthy horn growth as described for hoof cracks (pp. 48–50).

BRUISED SOLES

Bruised soles are a common cause of lameness. They usually result from a sharp object 'bruising' the bottom of the foot – standing on a sharp stone, for example. In severe cases abscesses may result, which will need paring by the vet, and poulticing (as with pricked soles). In severe cases either a vet or a farrier will be able to help: the shoe will have to be removed and the foot examined. In some cases it is found that a **corn** (a bruise in the heel region) is the problem, and this will have to be cut out. A special surgical shoe may be fitted to relieve the pressure of corns.

If a horse is particularly thin soled, it would be sensible to ask the farrier about fitting a leather pad under the shoe.

LAMINITIS

This very painful condition affecting the feet is notoriously suffered by ponies grazing spring grass. However, it can be brought about in all types of horse by a variety of causes, such as overfeeding or changes in diet. It usually affects only the front feet but may affect one or all four feet.

Symptoms which suggest laminitis include:

Stance typical of a horse with laminitis.

- Standing with the forelegs stretched forwards (this is known as the 'laminitic stance').
- Objection to moving.
- Objection to having the sole tested with hoof testers (pinchers).
- Heat in the affected feet.
- Rings on the feet, which indicate that the horse has suffered from laminitis in the past.
- Raised TPR, due to the pain.

Laminitis should be treated as an emergency and the vet must be called, because early treatment very often leads to a more successful outcome. While waiting for the vet, you can hose the feet with cold water to offer the horse some relief. Do not give pain-killing drugs, as this will prevent the vet from detecting the severity of the condition.

To manage laminitis, try to eliminate the cause: keep the pony off grass, or reduce your horse's feed, for example. The farrier will also become involved, as corrective trimming will often be necessary. Once suffered, laminitis is likely to occur again and you need to make a commitment to your horse's future management. Ask the vet about future exercise and feeding and follow the recommendations closely.

PEDAL OSTITIS

This condition affects the pedal bone in the horse's foot and it may occur as a sequel to laminitis or other foot problems. Look for the signs:

- Discomfort in both front feet.
- Discomfort when being ridden on hard ground.
- Relief when rested.
- Signs of pain when the hoof is tested with pincers.

This condition can only be diagnosed by a vet, who will have access to certain equipment.

NAVICULAR

Navicular disease affects the navicular bone in the horse's foot, hence its name. It usually affects horses rather than ponies. The causes are uncertain but it is a degenerative disease, which means that the condition deteriorates with time. At the time of writing there is no known cure for navicular.

Symptoms which might suggest navicular include:

- Stumbling and tripping up when ridden.
- Shuffling and shortened strides.
- Standing with one or other fore toe pointed forwards.
- Lame on and off.
- Lame when lunged on a circle.
- Shifting weight from one foot to the other when standing still.
- Boxy-looking hooves.

There are many treatments aimed at prolonging the working life of the horse but none, as yet, to cure the horse. The former include corrective farriery, drugs and 'nerve blocking', which is a surgical operation to take away the pain so that the horse is no longer lame. Seek veterinary help as soon as you suspect the condition. All of the above symptoms could be caused by some other condition but call the vet to put your mind at rest one way or another. If it turns out to be navicular, then it is only fair that the horse receives some form of pain relief.

SIDEBONES

These are 'false bones' which are caused by the hardening of the pedal bone cartilages. Sidebones usually develop in the front feet, although the horse is most likely to remain sound and in work. You may never be aware that your horse has sidebones, unless you can feel them towards the back of the foot, above the coronary band.

If you are unlucky your horse may go lame for a time, while sidebones are forming, but once they have formed there are usually no further problems. If the horse does go lame, box rest him and have your vet check him out.

Pointing the foot is a common sign of navicular.

CHAPTER 7

LAMENESS

If a horse is obviously lame, first check that there is not a simple reason such as a stone in the foot or a loose shoe.

If you suspect that there is a limb problem, check for heat by running your hand slowly down the leg until you can feel a slight rise in temperature. If you cannot feel any heat, it may be that lameness is due to a problem in the horse's back or shoulder, for instance.

Next, have your horse trotted up on a level surface. If he is lame in a foreleg, he will lift his head as the affected limb hits the ground; with the hindlegs, he will drop his head as the affected limb touches the ground.

COMMON LEG PROBLEMS

There are many leg problems which are very common amongst horses. As long as you learn to recognize them for what they are, and have the vet check them out if they seem to be troubling your horse, then they are not usually serious and you can deal with them yourself.

Swellings are usually a result of a knock while the horse is out in the field, or when rolling in the stable. A certain amount of bruising occurs, which needs to be dispersed as quickly as possible. You can usually feel heat at the site of the swelling. Apply cold treatment (see p. 34) as soon as possible; then after a day or so use alternate hot and cold treatment to reduce any swelling that still remains.

A **curb** is a swelling about 10cm (4in) below the hock at the back. It occurs as a result of the plantar ligament being sprained, usually due to excessive exercise or because of poor conformation. You will recognize a curb as a lump at the back of the hock. In the initial stages of a

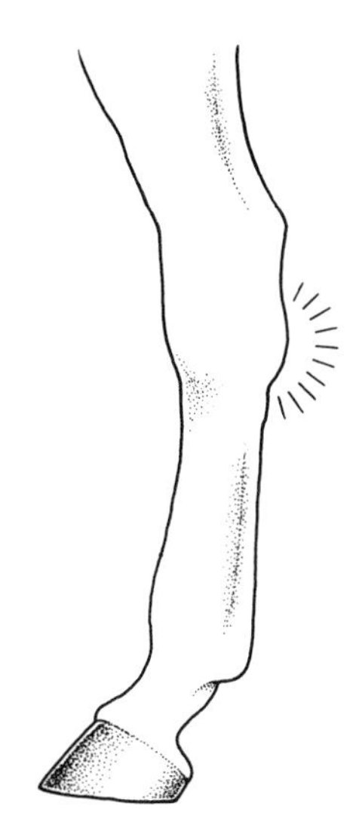

This is where you will see a curb.

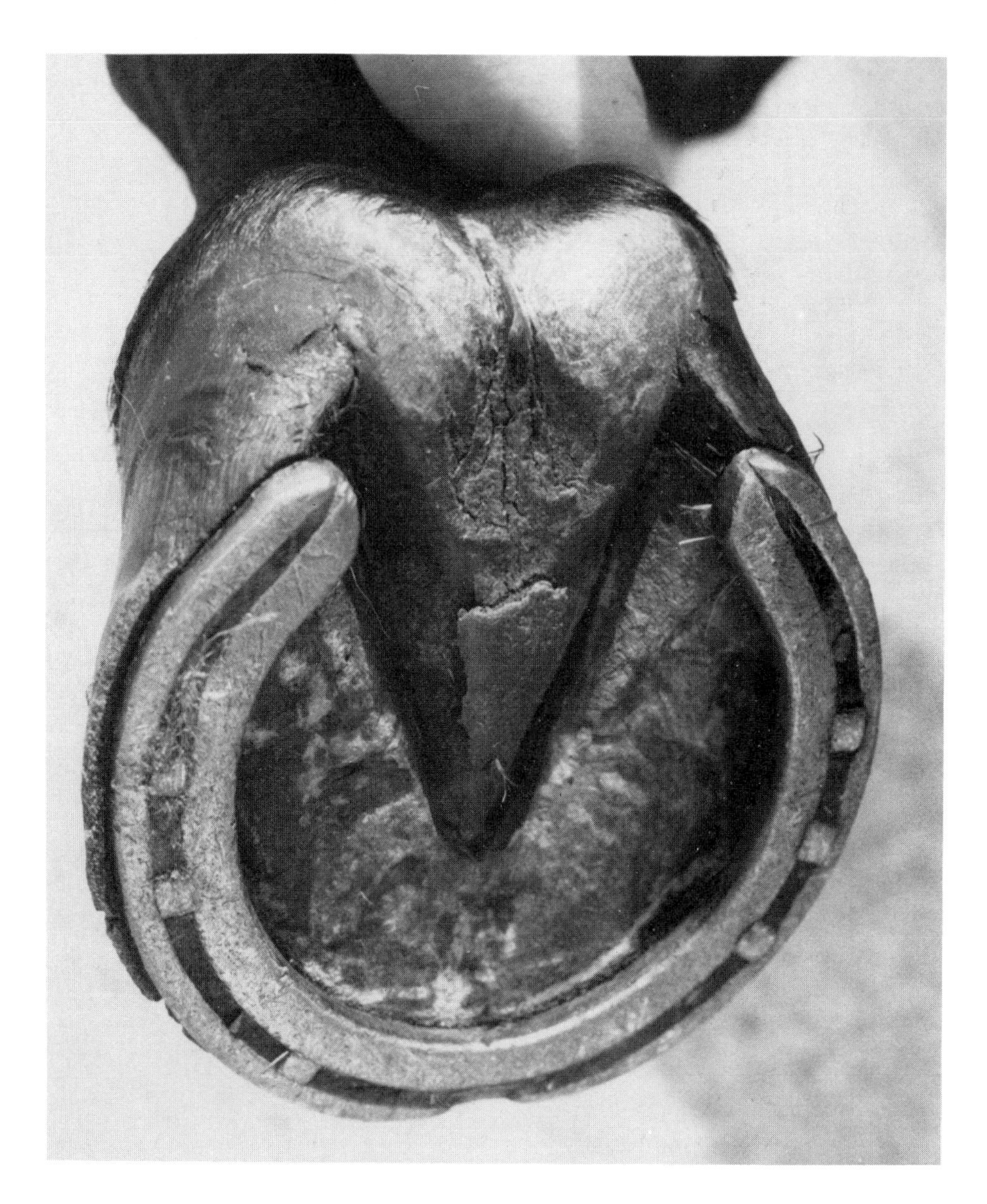

If a horse goes lame, check for an obvious sign first. This foot has overgrown its shoe and should have been attended to before now.

curb forming you may notice heat and swelling; your horse may stand with the heel raised, and may or may not be lame.

As soon as you notice a curb, rest your horse and use cold treatment. If there is lameness it might be necessary to apply an anti-inflammatory analgesic drug such as 'bute' (phenylbutazone). In the long term a mild blister may stimulate the ligament to heal. However, there will always be some permanent swelling.

Splints are bony enlargements of the splint bones resulting from strain to the ligaments. They usually appear on the inside of the forelegs as hard lumps, a quarter or half way down the lower leg. The horse may or may not go lame, according to the size of the splint, but there is likely to be heat and swelling at the site, which will be painful if squeezed.

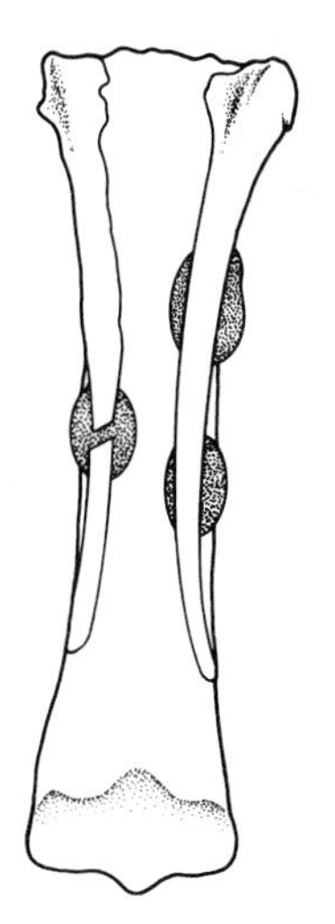

An internal view of how splints form on the splint bones.

Rest the horse immediately you suspect a splint, whether the horse is lame or not. Use cold treatment as early as possible and bandage the leg to offer some support. (Remember to bandage the other leg too.) An anti-inflammatory such as bute may also help to reduce inflammation. Once the initial painful stage has passed the swelling will reduce, but there will always be a hard, permanent lump or 'splint'.

To prevent splints from occurring in the first place:

- Avoid working young horses on the roads too much.

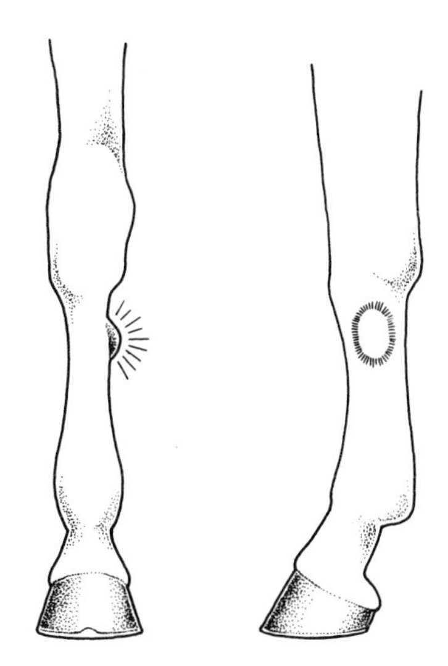

How splints look from the outside.

- Fit brushing boots for schooling and lungeing.
- Ensure that the horse's feet are attended to regularly by the farrier.

Strains, when they affect the tendons, can put a horse out of work for months. The horse will be very lame and the affected area will be hot, swollen and painful to the

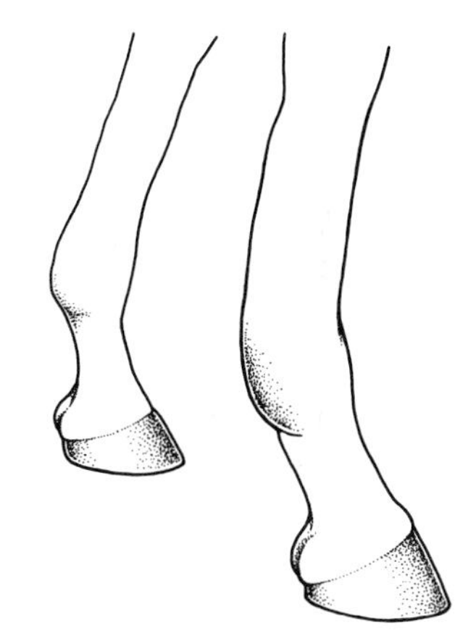

Sprained tendon.

touch. Rest the horse immediately and call the vet. In the meantime, apply ice packs. Your vet will probably advise you to keep up the cold treatment for a while and put on a pressure bandage, though there are other ways to treat injured tendons these days – through physiotherapy, for example (see pp. 37–8).

Where it is difficult to apply an ice pack (such as a hock) you should cold hose the area. Liniments can be applied to awkward places such as thighs and shoulders.

Puffy limbs are suffered by many horses when they are stabled overnight. The puffiness usually goes down with exercise and does not cause the horse any trouble. However, if your horse's limbs are not usually puffy, then investigate further: the cause may be overfeeding, a blow, or possibly improper kidney function.

Windgalls are pockets of fluid around the fetlock joints. Sometimes they can be pushed through from the inside of the leg to the outside. They may appear after rest and disappear with work or vice versa, or they may be permanent. They do not usually cause lameness, and no treatment is necessary. If your horse does go lame, further investigation is needed to establish the cause.

Thoroughpins are similar to windgalls, except that they appear over the hocks. Any steps taken to reduce them are usually only for cosmetic reasons – on a show horse for instance.

Capped hocks and elbows are caused by knocks. Once a capped hock or elbow is established, it is extremely difficult to reduce the resulting thickening. You can try applying a topical application, but it is unlikely to get rid of it altogether. Physiotherapy may help if used early enough, but prevention is certainly better than cure here, so make sure that your horse has a deep bed and a large enough box. A sausage boot may help to prevent a capped elbow.

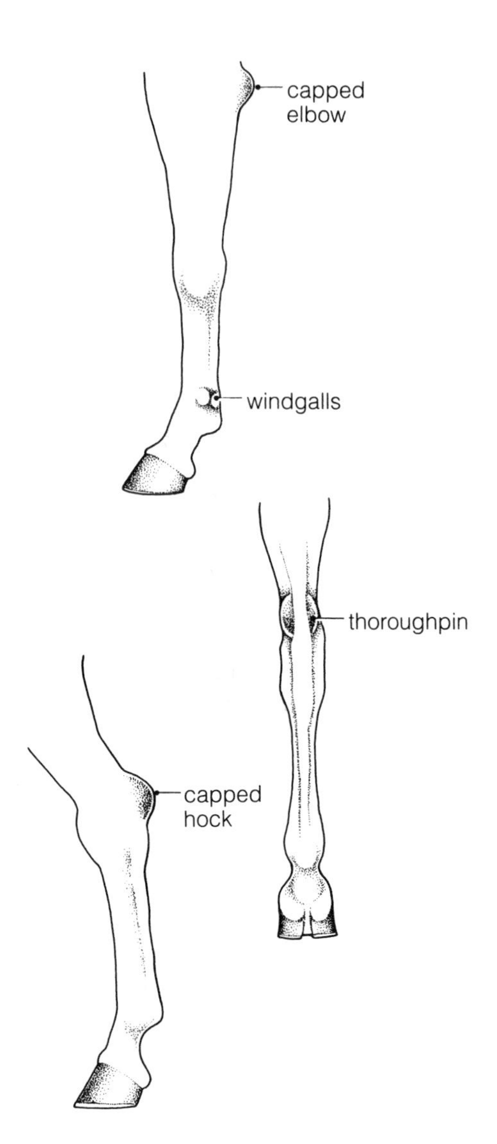

Fractures are emergencies. Always call the vet immediately when a fracture is suspected, and keep the

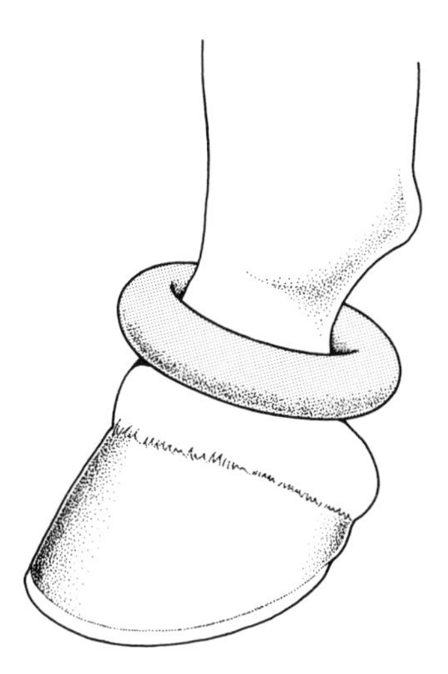

A sausage boot may help to prevent capped elbows.

horse still in the meantime. The chances of recovery will depend on where the break is, and how bad it is.

AZOTURIA

This used to be known as Monday morning disease as it often occurred following a day off (Sunday). It is a condition of muscular spasm, similar to the 'cramps' some people suffer from. It can affect just the quarters or the whole body.

If a horse is reluctant to walk out of the box, or starts to become stiff out on a ride or suddenly stops dead and refuses to move, it may be because the muscles are going into spasm and movement is extremely painful.

A horse that has had an azoturia attack will be more susceptible to it in the future. It is not fully understood why horses suffer from this ailment, but it is very important that you observe a strict feeding and exercise pattern for your horse. After carrying out tests, the vet will be the best one to advise you on how to proceed.

Azoturia – immediate action

Do not force your horse to walk home, but dismount immediately and just let him stand still. He may start to sweat, so try to keep him warm – use your coat if you cannot get hold of anything else. The pain may start to ease off, in which case you can walk your horse back home slowly or, if you can summon help, call for a vet and arrange to have your horse transported home in a trailer.

LYMPHANGITIS

This condition is usually attributed to an infection of some sort, perhaps the result of a small injury which went unnoticed. The horse's limbs (usually, but not always, the hindlimbs) start to swell from the pastern upwards. Within a day they may swell up to double their normal size, which is quite alarming. The horse will probably be reluctant to move, and you may see a fluid seeping from the affected leg or legs. You may also notice some, all or none of these symptoms:

- A rise in the horse's temperature.
- Sweating and/or trembling.
- Blowing.
- Loss of appetite.

This condition needs veterinary treatment, which is likely to include antibiotics and anti-inflammatory drugs. A horse that has had lymphangitis will be more prone to further attacks and the legs may then become permanently thickened.

ARTHRITIS

Arthritis is inflammation of a joint. Any of the joints in the body can be affected, especially if they have had their fair share of work through the years. This is why the condition appears more frequently in older competition and hunting horses. The affected joints are often warm, swollen and painful.

The only way to be sure that a horse has arthritis is for the vet to X-ray the problem site. If arthritis is diagnosed, then the job is one of management rather than cure. Initially the horse will find relief from cold-hosing and rest, but in the long term you must look towards managing the condition by relieving the pain with anti-inflammatory drugs. Ask your vet about the other treatments available that are aimed at helping an arthritic horse to remain in work.

CHAPTER 8

DIGESTIVE DISORDERS

It can be very distressing to find a horse lying down, rolling or kicking in pain, but you must keep calm and try to discover the cause as quickly as possible.

COLIC

If you discover your horse acting oddly in the stable or field, a prime suspect for the cause is colic. This term describes abdominal pain which comes from the digestive system or, in the case of renal colic, from the kidneys. It can vary from a mild case to an extremely painful and distressing one.

Horses seem to be more susceptible to colic than other animals and most cases of colic are attributed to certain causes:

- Worm infestation, where the horse has not been given regular wormers, or the appropriate type for a particular problem.
- Irregular feeding.
- Drinking large quantities of cold water while the horse is still hot.
- Sudden changes of diet.
- Poor quality food.
- Incomplete mastication of food due to poor teeth.
- Anxiety or stress.

Signs of colic

Horses with colic may be standing or lying down. They will be generally uneasy, possibly sweating, and will often look towards the stomach and perhaps try to kick at it with the hindlegs. They may paw the ground, rub the tail or box walk, in an attempt to relieve the discomfort. Many horses with colic will go down and get up frequently, and some will roll violently. By doing so they are capable of twisting their intestines ('twisted gut') and the consequences can be fatal.

They may frequently attempt to urinate and only be able to pass small amounts or even none at all. They may also attempt to pass droppings but find that they are incapable of doing so, or can only pass small amounts and/or large quantities of wind.

Colic in foals is quite common within the first few days of life. This is due to retention of meconium, the faecal material in the foal's bowel at birth. Colostrum (the mare's first milk) has a lubricant effect and this is often enough to relieve the situation. However, if the foal keeps straining without passing the meconium, or lies down with head stretched backwards, then veterinary intervention will be required.

Colic – immediate action

If you suspect that your horse has colic:

- Take the temperature – it does not usually rise above normal.
- Check the pulse. This may rise in relation to the amount of pain being experienced.
- Do *not* give a colic drench, or anything to eat.
- If he is lying down but not rolling, do not get him up: this is his way of dealing with the pain.
- If he is restless in the box, walk him around on a bridle for five or ten minutes on a soft surface (the paddock or a sand school, for example). However, if your horse keeps trying to throw himself to the ground, it will be safer to keep him in his box, with a deep bed if that is possible, or let him loose in an enclosed school, rather than risk injury.

If your horse seems to be finding relief quickly, keep a close eye on him. If he starts to urinate or pass droppings freely, or stops getting down and up and pawing at his own stomach or the ground, then these are all good signs that the pain is decreasing.

When to call the vet

Most cases of colic are not serious, so do not panic. However, if your horse does not start to improve quickly then it is better to call the vet sooner, rather than later, as you can never be sure whether it is really serious or not. If by the time your vet arrives your horse is quite happy and quietly munching on his hay, the vet will be just as pleased as you are.

Always call your vet, stating it is an emergency in any of the following circumstances:

- The pulse rate exceeds 45–50.
- The eye membranes are deeper than a salmon-pink (although bear in mind what is normal for your horse)
- The horse does not find any relief from what appears to be a mild attack within half an hour.
- The horse is obviously distressed or violent.
- The horse is rolling violently.
- The horse is attempting to pass urine or droppings, but cannot.

Frequently, all that is needed is a painkiller administered by the vet to relax the horse and relieve pain, until the whole episode passes. However, the vet will examine the horse fully and take whatever further action is necessary.

Have the following information ready:

- Whether or not the horse has passed any droppings. If so, take a note of the time and keep the droppings for the vet to examine.

- Whether the horse's stomach has been making any funny sounds. If so, what were they like?
- Whether you have changed the horse's diet, or turned him out on to grass for the first time in a while.
- Whether the horse is in constant pain, or only seems to be in pain on and off.

CHOKE

'Choke' is a condition in which food has caused an obstruction in the horse's oesophagus (throat). Various signs might alert you to the condition:

- Uneasiness and difficulty in swallowing.
- Coughing to try to remove the obstruction.
- Contracting and extending the neck.
- Making low grunting sounds.
- Box walking.
- Green-brown fluid dripping down the nostrils.
- Drooling at the mouth.
- Rubbing the head and neck.

Prevention

Usually choke occurs when a greedy horse comes into the stable to be fed, having been out all day. Typically he will dive into his feeding trough and devour his food rapidly, not waiting to chew it up properly. Within seconds he can be showing the signs of choke and it will depend on how bad the blockage is as to how quickly it will pass, or whether it will need veterinary attention. Sometimes the blockage may only be a few centimetres (an inch or so) in length and if the horse had consumed most of his feed before the blockage occurred, this will pass into the stomach and be digested as normal. If on the other hand the blockage occurs from the first mouthful, the horse may continue to eat until he can physically do so no longer, and the food just stacks up in front of the blockage. It is often possible to feel a hard mass of food along the throat in such cases.

Choke – immediate action

If a horse shows signs of choke, wait for ten minutes to see if the obstruction passes of its own accord (which in many cases it will). If not already in a stable, bring the horse in, away from other horses. *Do not* give anything to eat or drink. Keep a very close eye on the horse and **if there is no recovery after ten minutes, call your vet forthwith.** The horse may need an injection to relax and so allow the obstruction to disperse more easily. Sometimes it may be necessary to pass a stomach tube down the horse's throat to clear the blockage.

After the blockage has cleared, the throat may be a little sore. Only give soft mashes and allow the horse to eat grass in preference to hay. If there is no alternative, hay must be soaked before being fed.

- First of all, try to establish whether your horse is greedy because of hunger, or is just plain greedy! If a horse is hungry when coming in from the field, he is not getting enough sustenance from the grazing and should be supplied with hay while in the field.
- If feeding in the field with other horses, place the feeding bowls far apart to prevent a horse from feeling threatened, which will encourage him to bolt his food.
- Do not put your horse's feed into his stable before bringing him in. Bring your horse in first and allow him to munch at his hay for an hour before feeding.
- If he still dives into his food, then place a salt lick on top of his food, which will make him slow down.
- Feed from a bowl on the floor rather than a manger over the door or at chest height. Include chaff in the feed to encourage your horse to chew the food properly before swallowing.
- Always soak sugar beet for 24 hours before feeding and consider changing from nuts to mixes if your horse has suffered from choke on more than one occasion.
- Cut up carrots and apples *lengthwise*, and not into round pieces or cubes which might become lodged in the throat.
- Ensure that your horse's teeth do not need rasping and that there is no gum disease or sores in the mouth. A sore mouth may prevent the horse from chewing food properly.

DIARRHOEA

Diarrhoea can be mild, in which case it usually clears up without complications, or it can be severe, in which case veterinary intervention is necessary.

If the cause of the diarrhoea is known (your horse always get excited when at shows and develops diarrhoea, or you have suddenly turned your horse out on to lush grass, for example) then there is no need to be alarmed. You should be methodical in your treatment of diarrhoea, though:

- First, put the horse in the stable.
- Provide good quality hay.
- Provide plenty of fresh, clean water.
- Do not feed succulents (apples or carrots, for example) or sugar beet.
- Add electrolytes to the water, but ensure that the horse will happily drink them before leaving him. It is more important that he drinks water, so do not use electrolytes if he obviously dislikes the taste.
- Gradually reintroduce your horse to grass, if this was the cause. Limit grazing to short periods at a time.

If the cause is not known, then call your vet as the diarrhoea may be a symptom of another condition. Always call your vet in the following circumstances:

- When a foal has diarrhoea.
- If a horse with diarrhoea develops

a temperature and generally seems unwell.

- If the diarrhoea does not seem to be clearing up within 36 hours, although the horse seems generally in good health.

Causes

There are various causes of diarrhoea including:

- A change in diet.
- Excitement.
- Nervousness (this may be evident to you, but you may not know why).
- Worms (when did you last worm your horse?).
- Administration of antibiotics by your vet for another condition (has your horse had any antibiotics?).
- An infection (you will have no way of knowing without an examination by your vet).
- Poisoning (are there any poisonous plants in the field? Have you recently treated the stables or fences? Have there been any strangers around who might have given your horse something? Have you been giving your horse any drugs without your vet's knowledge?).

GRASS SICKNESS

Grass sickness is a very traumatic disease of the nervous system that affects the horse's alimentary canal – the tube which extends the length of the horse's body from lips to anus, in which digestion of food occurs.

Unfortunately the condition is fatal, there is no cure and the only way to proceed after diagnosis is to have your horse put down quickly to prevent further suffering.

Symptoms include: depression, rapid pulse, rapid weight loss, inability to swallow food or water, dehydration, food regurgitated and running from both nostrils, lack of gut sounds, severe colic.

POISONING

Poisoning is not common among horses, but it can happen, and there are several general causes:

- Eating a poisonous plant.
- Eating contaminated feed.
- Licking something poisonous (newly treated fencing, for example).
- Accidental overdose of drugs.
- Deliberate poisoning (this is known as 'nobbling' in racing circles).
- Stinging by a bee, wasp or hornet – some unlucky horses react very violently.

Thankfully, horses have a very delicate sense of smell and taste and most will spit out something that does not taste right, unless they have been forced to eat it because they are starving. However, it is obviously best to ensure that there is nothing poisonous in a horse's field, hay, feed or stable, remembering that some horses will lick newly creosoted fences and painted stables.

Is this horse ill? Has it been poisoned? Don't leave it to chance – check it out.

A horse suffering from mild poisoning may show signs very similar to those of colic (see pp. 61–2). However, in serious cases the horse can die within minutes of having eaten something highly poisonous, *although this is rare.*

The only action to take as soon as poisoning is suspected is to call your vet immediately and emphasize that it is a matter of very great urgency.

Poisonous plants

The greatest risk of poisoning comes from certain plants that may be present in a horse's field.

Horses avoid most poisonous plants whilst they are still growing but are more likely to eat them if there is little else to eat, or if the plants have died and wilted. Good pasture management is essential: horses that are provided with good, clean pasture are less likely to eat what they should not. Regularly check the fields for poisonous plants. If you find any, or anything you are not sure about, then dig them out, root and all. Owners of land which contains injurious weeds, plants or trees are legally responsible and have a duty to protect animals from a horrible and unnecessary death. Anybody who looks after horses should learn how to identify poisonous plants.

Ragwort

Ragwort is one of the most common poisonous plants. In the early stages of growth it has a dense rosette of irregular, dark green, jagged-edged leaves, and this is the best time to remove it. From late June it grows taller – anything up to about 100cm (3ft) high – with yellow, daisy-like

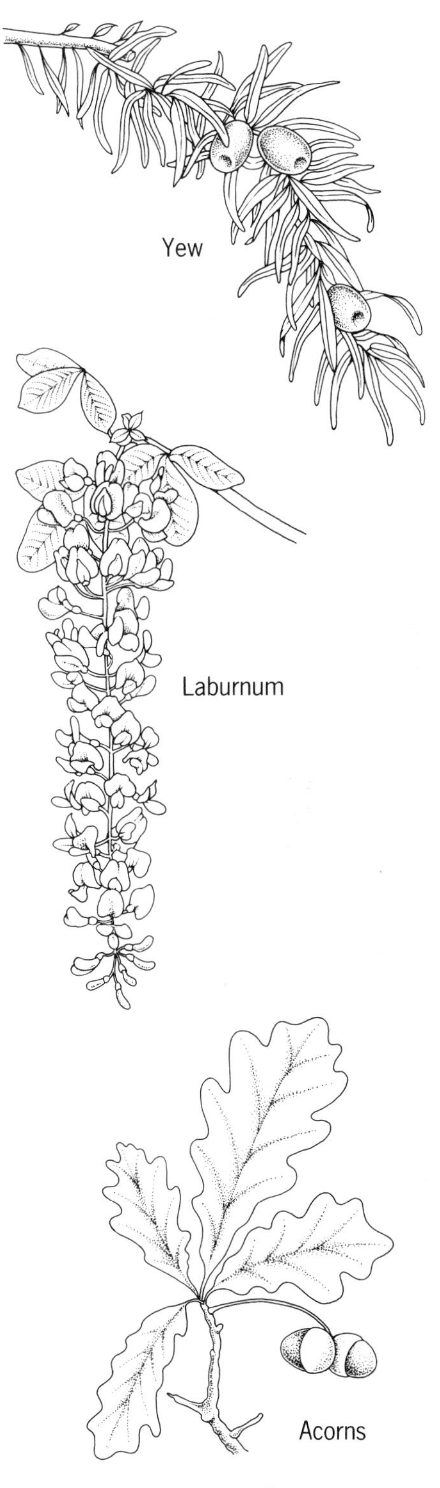

Some common poisonous plants.

heads. It is very poisonous to horses and causes chronic liver damage. Close grazing and low fertility of land, both of which are common where horses are intensely grazed, appear to encourage its growth.

The effects of ragwort poisoning are cumulative, so you might not notice any signs until weeks or months after the horse has eaten it. If your horse begins to lose weight in spite of feeding well, and seems lethargic or depressed, or shows regular signs of pain in the abdomen, have a veterinary check.

Other poisonous plants

There are other poisonous plants or trees which can cause problems if they hang over into the field. Yew and laburnum are extremely poisonous: either fence them off so that there is no possibility of a horse getting at them, or remove them altogether. One mouthful of any part of these trees is enough to kill a horse within minutes.

The oak tree is another cause of trouble: horses that eat its acorns (and some horses acquire a taste for them) can become very ill. Again, fence the trees off, taking the spread of the branches into account when erecting the fence.

Fortunately, horses will rarely touch these trees, but they may pick at clippings or fallen debris. Make sure that neighbours do not leave any of these in the paddock – and check yourself to make certain.

CHAPTER 9

COUGHS, COLDS AND 'FLU

Coughs and colds are problems that affect the respiratory system and the way the horse breathes. Other problems, such as COPD (chronic obstructive pulmonary disease) and strangles can affect a horse's respiratory system. Many conditions which affect the respiratory system have similar symptoms. It is therefore important to try to establish what differentiates one condition from another, when trying to decide what is wrong with a horse that starts coughing, or whose glands become enlarged, for instance.

COUGHING

Many horses cough and by far the most common cause is an allergy to stable dust. This is known as a respiratory allergy and is different from a cough produced as a result of an infectious disease such as equine influenza ('flu). Dust allergies will have to be managed, while in the case of 'flu a horse will recover to normal after a period, provided that the correct care is given.

A horse may also cough for many other reasons, such as worm infestation, so a correct veterinary diagnosis should be made before any treatment is given.

CHRONIC OBSTRUCTIVE PULMONARY DISEASE (COPD)

COPD, often known as **broken wind**, is probably the most common cause of chronic coughing in horses. It is caused by an allergy to stable dust and/or fungal spores in hay and straw. Some horse become hypersensitive to the spores when inhaling them and will experience asthma-type symptoms.

It is important to know how to prevent sensitization, if at all possible, as there is no cure once the condition is established. The key to both prevention and treatment is good stable management, providing an environment that is as free from dust and spores as possible. This is known as a 'clean air regime'.

COPD usually develops over a period of time, and a horse may seem well but will gradually become less tolerant of exercise. A horse that is only mildly affected will still benefit from exercise, though, which will help to keep the respiratory system in good order.

Observations

The affected horse may have an increased respiratory rate and give the occasional cough at the start of exercise, or when trotted up. You might see a slight nasal discharge, especially first thing in the morning. This discharge may get worse as the condition progresses; it will become more apparent after exercise, turning from a slight milk-white to a thick, yellow one.

Once COPD is established the horse will start to cough more when being exercised and in the stable, and may cough up lumps of mucus. There has to be an increase in respiratory effort, which is seen as an extra 'lift' in the abdominal muscles when inhaling. By this stage a 'heave line' may be visible along the lower edge of the abdomen.

Action

When a horse pulls at dry hay, fungal spores are released. Soaking the hay for several hours in clean water swells the spores and helps to reduce the number of spores inhaled. Only soak the amount of hay that will be eaten overnight, as soaked hay soon turns sour. Feeding vacuum packed and proprietary dust-free forages is more effective in reducing inhalation of spores than feeding soaked hay.

Straw bedding is not suitable for a horse that has COPD as it often contains high levels of fungal spores. As an alternative to straw you can use woodshavings, shredded paper, rubber matting or one of the various proprietary dust-free beddings.

Concentrates can also contain fungal spores, and should therefore be dampened before feeding. Feeding a horse from the floor will also help to prevent the inhalation of any spores and will allow some drainage of the mucus that collects in the trachea.

Stable design plays an important part in the management of COPD. Good ventilation is essential and there should be a good flow of clean air through the building. In conventional stables, make sure that there is a window and adequate ventilation to ensure a good air flow. Ridge-roof ventilators and louvres between stables in a row enhance ventilation, but also allow dust and spores to filter through to your horse's stable if the next-door horse is not on a clean air regime.

Of course the ultimate 'clean air regime' is keeping a horse out-of-doors. A horse that is diagnosed as having COPD should be turned out as much as possible – all the time is the ideal – and thus kept away from any hay or straw, or other materials that create dust or spores. In winter the outdoor horse obviously needs rugging and access to a shelter for protection from adverse weather conditions.

PASTURE ASSOCIATED PULMONARY DISEASE (PAPD)

Some horses are thought to be allergic to certain pollens and show signs of COPD while out at grass. This is known as pasture associated pulmonary disease or PAPD. Oilseed rape has been suspected as a possible cause of this condition, although there is not yet any scientific proof. If a horse shows signs of COPD while out at grass, try to prevent further sensitization to pollens by keeping your horse away from them as much as possible.

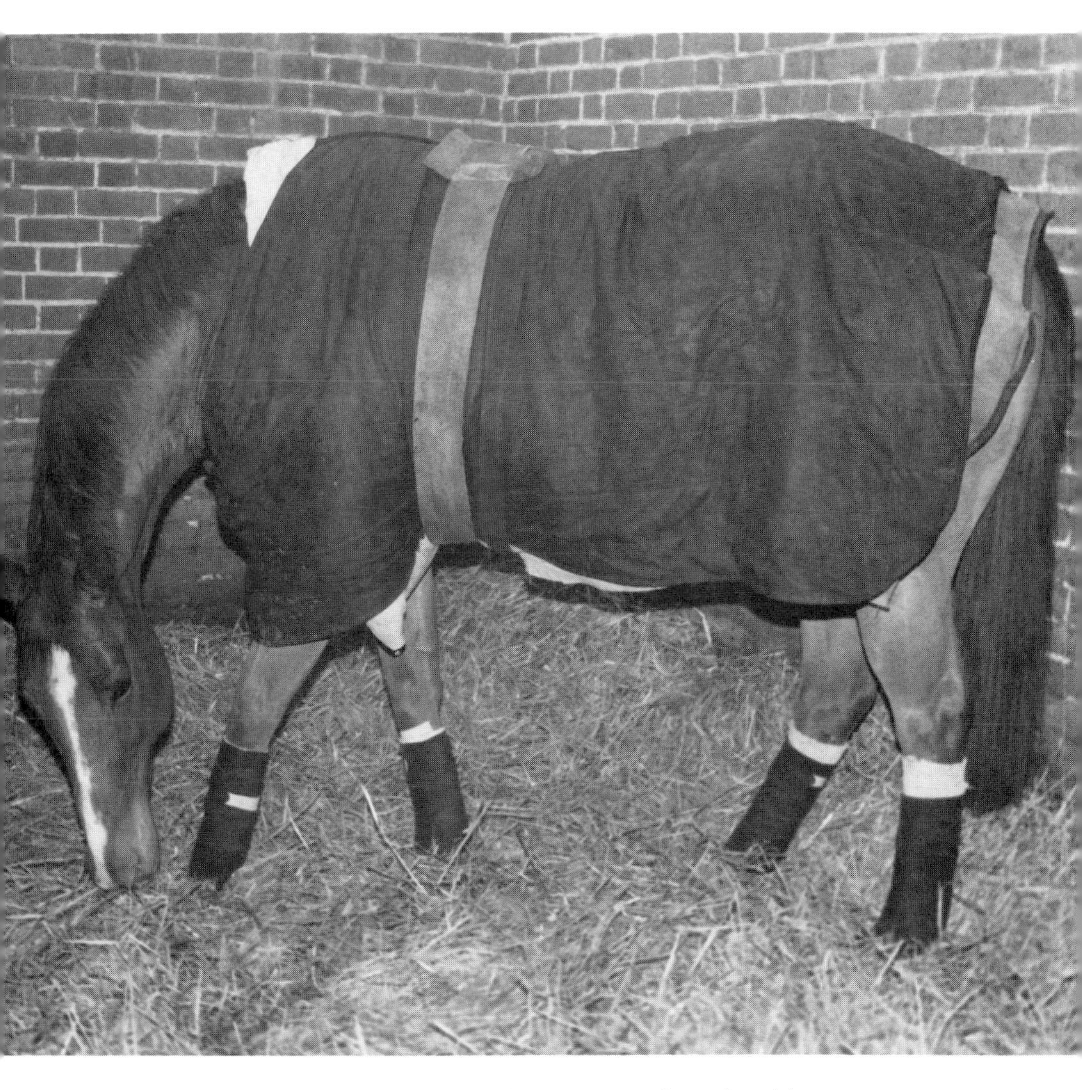

A horse with equine influenza should be kept warm and comfortable.

EQUINE INFLUENZA

Just like you, a horse can suffer from influenza, and will feel as you might – very tired and irritable and generally unwell and uncomfortable. A horse that is suspected of having 'flu should be isolated immediately and examined closely. **Then call for the vet without delay.**

There are several signs to look for:

- A raised temperature. This might be anything from 38.6 to 41°C (101.5–106°F).
- Loss of appetite.
- A dry, rasping cough.
- A watery discharge or, if the horse has been suffering for some days, a thicker discoloured discharge.

- Enlarged glands. These can be observed between the horse's upper cheek bones and neck, and under the lower jaw.
- Watery or weeping eyes.
- Shivering.

Action

A horse that has 'flu needs to be kept warm in a stable with a good deep bed, rugged up and wearing stable bandages. Try to prevent any draughts, but ensure that there is still plenty of ventilation.

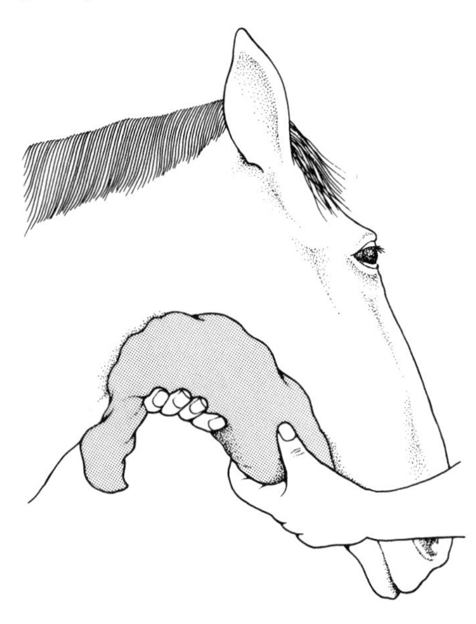

Holding warm cloths around the throat and glands will help to soothe a sore throat.

A horse that seems to have difficulty in swallowing may have a sore throat. Placing warm cloths over the glands and throat will give some relief. Always make sure that there is plenty of fresh, clean drinking-water, although this should not be too cold.

To treat any nasal discharge, put a cloth that has been soaked in hot water in the bottom of a muzzle (use the leather type which is not totally enclosed – an enclosed fibreglass one will restrict breathing if a cloth is placed in the bottom), on which you can put a few drops of eucalyptus oil

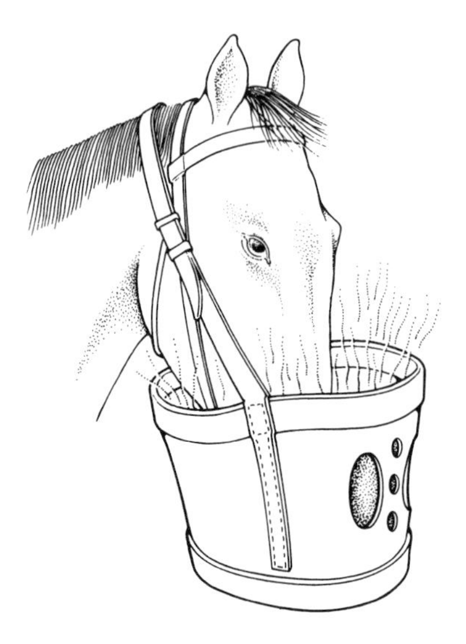

Steam inhalation is good for coughs and congestion.

or Friar's balsam. This will also help to loosen any congestion. If you do not have a muzzle, you can tie a small hessian sack on to a headcollar and place the steaming cloth in this. Make sure that the cloth is not so hot that it will scald the horse's nose if he reaches down and touches it. Do not leave a horse unattended while using steam inhalation.

Once the temperature has gone down, the horse will benefit from being turned out, although still needing to be kept warm.

Once all of the symptoms have disappeared, give a further two weeks' rest before bringing the horse back into light work.

The importance of vaccination

It is essential that all horses living together, whether in the field or within the stable yard, are vaccinated regularly. It is also irresponsible to take unvaccinated horses to competitions, as they may carry the infection and pass it on. This is why most shows now insist on seeing a current certificate of vaccination. If all owners act responsibly and have all their horses vaccinated, then far fewer horses will ever suffer from this infectious influenza.

PNEUMONIA

Pneumonia may develop after 'flu and also for other reasons. Always be on the look-out, especially if a horse has had a long and tiring journey, or has had problems with swallowing. Pneumonia is not common in adult horses, but is seen more often in foals. It can develop as a result of drenches being inhaled, which is why vets no longer recommend that horse-owners drench their horses for conditions such as colic.

The signs of pneumonia are similar to those of 'flu, although additionally the horse may be breathing much faster and condition may drop rapidly. **Always call the vet if you suspect pneumonia**, and in the meantime keep your horse warm and stay with him for company.

SINUS INFECTIONS

Horses have large frontal sinuses on either side of the head which drain straight into the nasal cavity. These sinuses can easily become infected. When they do, the horse might seem a little head-shy and you will see a thick discharge coming down one or other of the nostrils. Usually a course of antibiotics from the vet will clear up the problem and you can also use steam inhalation (as with the 'flu) to give some relief. Feeding a horse from the floor will help the sinuses to drain and thus prevent them from becoming blocked.

STRANGLES

Strangles is a *highly infectious* respiratory infection, caused by bacteria. Symptoms are progressive and include:

- High temperature, often up to 40.6°C (105°F).
- Cough.
- Tiredness.
- Watery nasal discharge, turning to thick yellow.
- Increase in respiratory rate.
- Loss of appetite.
- Difficulty in swallowing.
- Loss of condition.
- Hard abscesses which are hot and extremely painful, under the throat and around the glands and which eventually burst open and ooze pus.

Once this stage has been reached the horse is over the worst and will start to recover.

Action

Call your vet, as anti-inflammatory drugs may be needed in the early stages of the disease. *Immediately*

Enlarged glands and a nasal discharge are two of the signs of strangles.

strangles is suspected isolate the horse in a well-ventilated box with a deep bed. Put into effect a clean air regime (see p. 69) to prevent any irritation from dust. Provide plenty of clean water, which will need changing frequently as pus may drop into the water when your horse drinks. As swallowing may be painful, only feed soft mashes and soaked hay.

The abscesses will burst eventually but you can aid the process by using hot formentation to ripen them until they rupture or your vet decides to lance them. Once they have burst, you should flush them out twice daily with a solution provided by your vet (probably diluted hydrogen peroxide).

Any nasal discharge should be cleaned away with clean, warm water and a soft sponge, and you can use steam inhalation (see p. 72) to offer relief from congestion, and to ease the draining of mucus and pus.

Do not bring your horse back into light work until two weeks after the abscesses have healed.

With strangles, you must make every effort to prevent the spread of infection to other horses. This means that only one person should deal with the infected horses and that person should not attend any other horse in the yard. Use separate buckets, feeding equipment, rugs, headcollars and troughs for each horse. Disinfect everything regularly, and again once the infection has passed, including your clothes as well as the horse's equipment. Do not take your horse to a competition until a month after recovery.

NOSEBLEED

Unlike humans, horses do not suffer from common nosebleeds. However, they do sometimes bleed from the nostril after exertion and this is thought to be caused by lung haemorrhage. Occasionally a nosebleed might be caused by an injury or a blow to the side of the face. In any event, **always have nosebleeds checked out by your vet,** who is the only one who can establish the true cause.

VIRUSES

The biggest worry to competitors is that their horse may get 'the virus' and lose form. In fact, horses suffer from many virus infections, which usually cause symptoms similar to mild equine 'flu (see pp. 71–2).

The most common virus to affect horses is equine herpes virus type 1 (EHV1), which is easily spread from horse to horse. Unlike 'flu, there is no effective vaccine and treatment is usually complete rest until the horse recovers.

CHAPTER 10

Skin Ailments and Allergies

The skin is a horse's first and main defence against infection, and it is very important that you keep it clean and healthy. If the skin gets damaged, there will be a weak point at which bacteria from the atmosphere can enter the body. The skin consists of many layers and although it is waterproof, it can be softened if it is continually damp – during a wet winter or spring, for example. This gives rise to conditions such as mud fever and rain-scald.

Dry, hot weather can bring its own problems, such as sweet itch. Some skin conditions, such as ringworm, appear at any time of the year so be on your guard and take preventive measures.

HYGIENE

A long-coated, ungroomed horse is a haven for all sorts of parasites and skin ailments. They can bury themselves in for the winter and have a great time causing a lot of damage underneath. Even horses that have been turned away for the winter should be brought in and given a brush down with a dandy brush. This will ensure that any cuts or developing ailments are spotted. During these regular sessions be on the look out for any parasites or any patches of the horse's coat that look as though they have been rubbed.

WINTER SKIN AILMENTS

Mud fever, **rain-scald** and **cracked heels** are all skin complaints that can affect a horse in the winter months. They are caused by a dermatitis bacterium (*Dermatophilus congolensis*) which thrives in damp, muddy conditions and produces scabby eczema-like symptoms which can be very painful for the horse.

The condition is known as mud fever when the legs are affected, rain-scald when the back is affected and cracked heels when symptoms are shown in the hollows of the pasterns. Mud fever is recognized by scabby lesions which can become inflamed and very painful. A horse with white legs will be more susceptible, and the pasterns are commonly affected. Cracked heels start as scurf and scabs in the hollow at the back of the pastern, which develop into painful cracks.

All these complaints commonly affect horses that are turned out into wet, muddy paddocks. Prolonged soaking softens the skin, enabling the bacterium to enter, and the abrasive

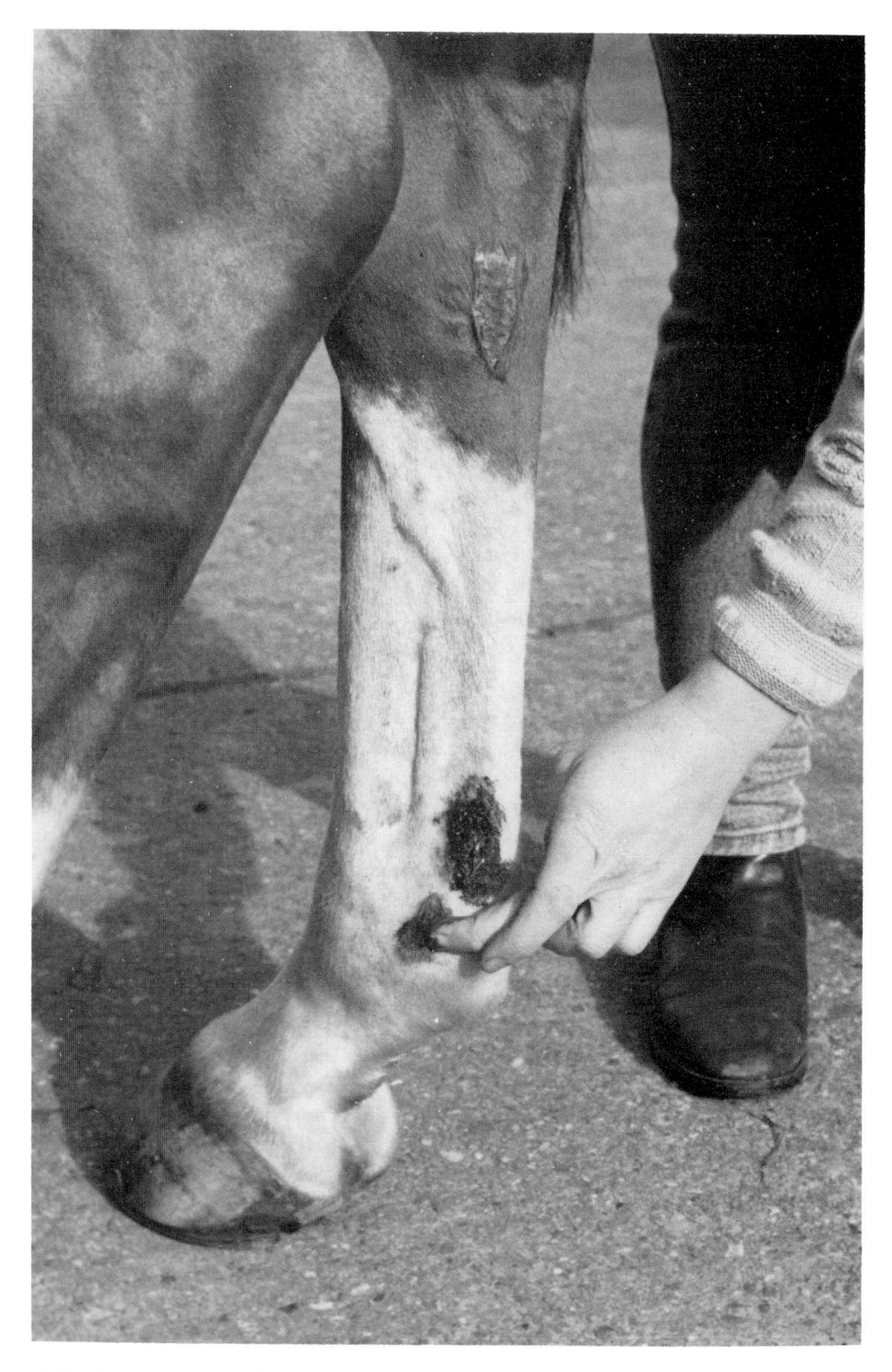

At the first signs of mud fever, clean away the scabs and apply a soothing ointment.

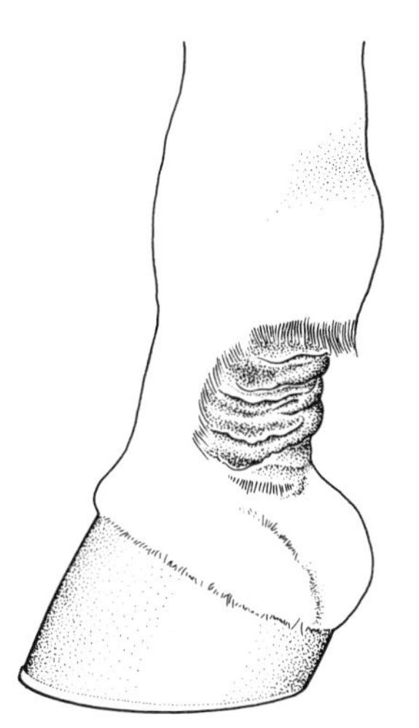

Cracked heels.

action of mud breaks the skin which then makes entry even easier.

The bacterium which causes mud fever has some fungus-like characteristics and can form spores which are capable of surviving on the horse's coat for many months, if not years. It can therefore flare up at any time and horses have shown symptoms of mud fever in the middle of summer.

Extreme vigilance is needed where a horse is susceptible to these skin conditions. Not only are they painful but they can also lead to more serious infections. For example, if mud fever is left untreated, it can spread up the legs to the flexor tendons and cause serious lameness.

Prevention

As with many complaints, prevention of mud fever and its associated conditions is better than cure. In the winter months a field gateway can turn into a quagmire. It is a good idea to put shale down in front of gates and water troughs or wherever else horses congregate, to prevent them from standing in vast areas of sloppy mud.

Keeping your horse dry and clean is of course desirable. Where this is not possible, apply a barrier cream such as zinc and castor oil or liquid paraffin to protect vulnerable areas such as heels and up over the pasterns before turning out in muddy conditions. If you know your horse to be susceptible try not to ride in muddy or wet areas, as prolonged contact with water and mud will encourage the bacteria to thrive.

Action

Keep a close eye on your horse and check him every day when you bring him in for grooming. If you need to hose mud off his legs, dry them gently but thoroughly afterwards. If the mud is dry, brush it off gently. Vigorous brushing with coarse bristles can cause more of the abrasions which allow the mud fever bacteria to enter.

Begin treatment at the very first sign of infection. Start by eliminating the cause: take the horse off the paddock and stable him.

Clip away any long hair from around the affected area and gently remove the scabs to expose the condition to the air. The scabs will be hard and crusty and removal of them may be extremely painful for the horse. To minimize the pain, firstly moisten the scabs by washing with an antibacterial soap and warm water. If the mud fever has been neglected you may need to soak the scabs for at least half an hour before trying to remove them. You can do this either by simply hosing them, by using a hose boot, or by tubbing with warm water.

When the scabs have been removed, the area will look very sore. Dry thoroughly by gently patting with clean cotton and gauze tissue. Apply a soothing antibiotic ointment twice daily. Ointments that contain corticosteroid help to reduce any inflammation, which may be a factor in more severe cases of the condition.

If bedding is likely to stick to the sore areas, stable bandage over a clean layer of cotton and gauze tissue. If possible allow the horse to stand unbandaged in a stable without bedding – rubber matting is ideal for this.

After a few days of such treatment the condition should be drying up nicely, with new hair already starting to grow. More severe cases may need poulticing before removing the scabs, as secondary bacterial infection often develops. The warm poultice should be squeezed out as much as possible as it will then draw out the infection and any remaining dirt. The warmth will help to increase the blood supply to the damaged area, which will promote healing and reduce inflammation. Once the poultice is removed, the condition can be treated as before. Where a secondary bacterial infection has developed, a course of antibiotics may be needed.

Rain-scald

If a horse is subjected to long periods of driving rain, the dermatophilus bacteria may be able to penetrate the softened skin. A horse that is left unrugged and without shelter from the rain is more likely to develop the condition. At first the coat starts to look 'starry' and slightly 'lifted' away from the skin. This is more obvious over the back, loins, shoulder and quarters. Large tufts of hair then become matted together, which are often referred to as 'paintbrush' lesions due to their spiky appearance. Once established these can be picked off, the lesions washed with antibacterial soap and left to dry, as with mud fever. The horse will need to be stabled until the condition has healed, and can then be turned out in a New Zealand rug in a field that has a shelter.

SWEET ITCH

This condition makes horses rub their manes and tails. It is caused by a reaction to the saliva of biting midges during all but the winter months. The severity of the condition varies from horse to horse; some will only rub occasionally, while others will rub themselves bald, causing open sores.

It is certainly a condition that should be prevented, or managed, rather than waiting for it to occur and then treating it. The midges that cause the trouble are more active around dusk and again around dawn. So if possible make sure the horse is stabled at these times.

If you cannot stable your horse there are other steps that you can take:

- Put a summer sheet on your horse while out in the field, making sure that it is secure.
- Use a linen hood, which covers half the head and the mane, and a linen tail guard, from 3.30 pm to 8.30 am.

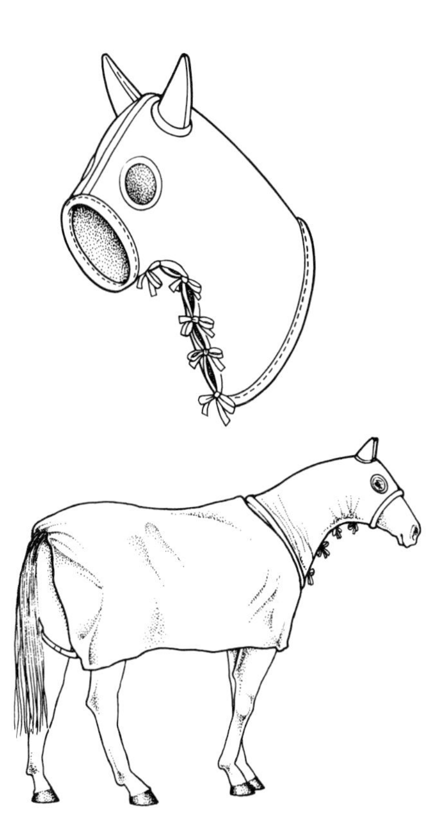

Protective clothing will help to prevent skin ailments if a horse is particularly susceptible to them.

- Keep your horse away from grazing areas that have ponds nearby.
- Feed your horse garlic.
- Use a long-acting fly repellent.

Action

If sweet itch develops, you should begin to treat it immediately.

Obtain a good shampoo from your vet, preferably a spray-on kind which will get right into the hair. Rub it well in to help to remove any scurf and scabs. Be careful to rinse it out thoroughly, or else the horse might start rubbing as a result of shampoo irritation. Repeat every week while the horse suffers from the condition and after washing apply a soothing lotion such as benzyl benzoate. Rub this lotion in twice a day as it will also discourage midges from biting and will give your horse some relief. Make sure that you rub it well into all areas, including the underside of the mane and tail.

LICE

Lice are small, dark-coloured parasites which can live on a horse all year round. Although they are visible to the naked eye, you may only realize that they are there when the horse starts to rub. Lice bite horses and suck their blood, which causes great irritation and in some cases a horse will rub until bald patches occur. Lice are contagious: you should not allow your horse to come into contact with any others until you are certain that you have eradicated the parasites from the coat.

A horse's coat should not be allowed to get into a filthy, matted

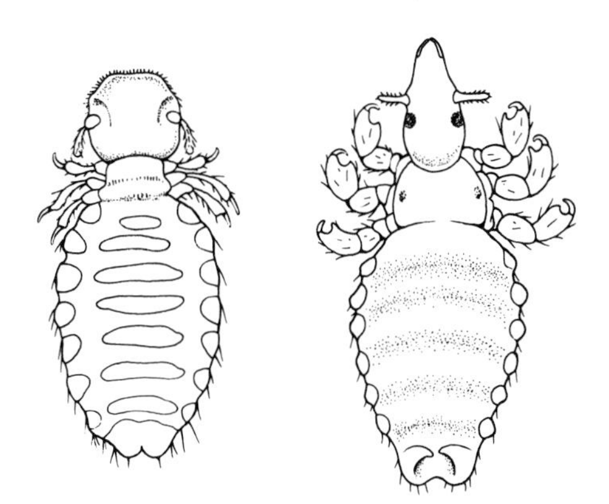

Two types of lice which live on the horse; these are visible to the naked eye if you look closely enough.

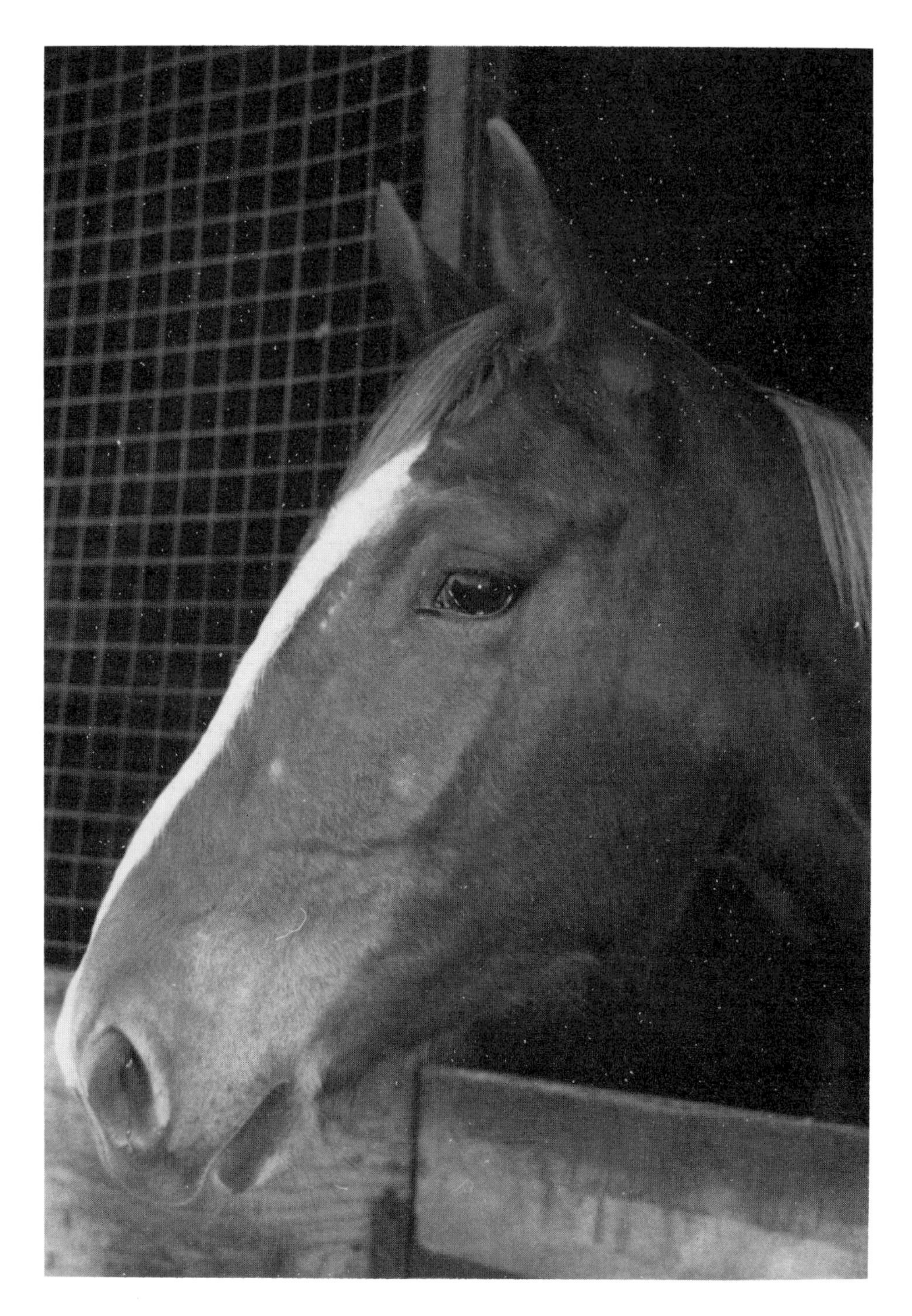

Why are these bald patches developing? If you don't know check to see if your horse has lice or some other skin complaint. Early detection leads to a speedier recovery.

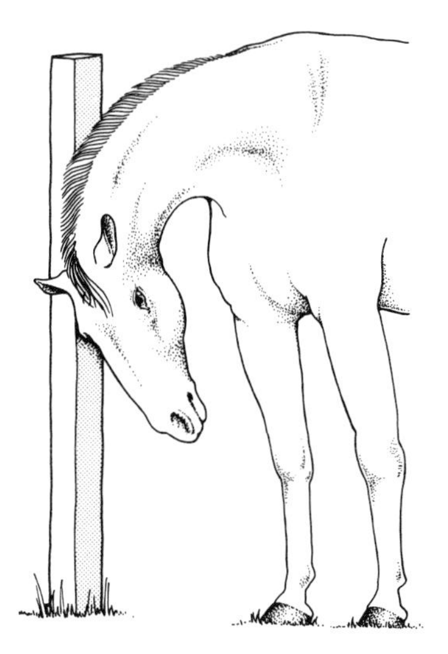

A horse that starts to rub may have skin parasites.

state before the lice are noticed. As soon as you see them, give the horse a thorough dusting with a good louse powder. This will need to be repeated to kill off new parasites as they hatch out. As some lice feed on scurf and skin debris, clean your horse properly to make sure they go without a meal.

Be especially vigilant in the cold months of the year as lice are much more active then than in hot weather.

BOTS

These parasites use the horse's hair and skin as a means of entry into the body. Bot flies lay their eggs on to a horse's skin, usually on the lower limbs, where they are unwittingly licked up by the horse and swallowed. The eggs then develop into fully fledged worms inside the body. Use a bot-fly comb and a good stiff brush to remove them from the horse's legs as soon as they appear, and ensure that you adhere strictly to your horse's worming programme.

WARTS

Two types of wart appear on horses: papilloma and sarcoids.

Papilloma are small warts which are most commonly seen around a youngster's face. They are usually quite harmless, although unsightly, and they almost always disappear of their own accord as the horse matures, so no treatment is necessary.

Sarcoids are a larger type of wart or tumour which can appear anywhere on the horse's body and often down the legs. If they occur in a place that is likely to cause problems it may be best to remove them, although they are more unsightly than life-threatening. If they are flat and small, try using a normal human wart ointment. Sometimes they can be removed by tying a tight rubber band around them, although this is best done by a vet.

Larger sarcoids may require surgical removal, although this is usually only necessary for cosmetic reasons and there is a 50 per cent chance that they will reappear. If it is decided that a sarcoid needs removing because of health reasons, the vet may try other forms of treatment.

RINGWORM

This condition is caused not by a worm but by a fungus. The condition is named for the round bald patches that develop, although in many cases the bald patches are not actually round.

There is little that can be done to

prevent ringworm, which is very contagious and has a long incubation period. A horse that has been in contact with a contagious horse might not develop the condition until three months later.

As soon as you notice ringworm, you must isolate the horse. Treat the condition by using a topical antifungal skin wash, all over the horse, three times at three-day intervals and then again two weeks later if necessary. If the condition is established, treat with griseofulvin (although this must not be used for brood mares) by putting this antifungal drug into the horse's feed for 7–10 days. Ensure strict standards of hygiene by disinfecting all tack and stables with a fungicidal solution and do not touch other horses without first disinfecting your own hands and clothes.

The first sign of ringworm might be several small tufts of hair. These soon develop into raised clumps which easily fall off and continue to do so until you see small hairless patches of crusty skin, which may or may not exude a small amount of serum. They commonly appear around the girth and saddle areas, or anywhere that tack meets the skin, but they will often spread all over the body.

Often you will just see the typical type of 'ring' appear and spread all over the horse's coat. Once a stage has been reached where the patches are dry and scaly, it will take about four weeks for the hair to regrow. Use coconut oil to encourage the hair to grow back properly.

URTICARIA

This is more commonly known as nettle rash and has various causes:

- A reaction to fly bites.
- A reaction to something in the horse's diet – often barley.
- A reaction to nettles or irritating undergrowth or bedding.
- A reaction to some drugs.

A horse with urticaria will develop raised patches of fluid under the skin. These can vary in size and number. Sometimes they develop and disappear within a few hours. At other times they may be more persistent. It is sensible to try to pinpoint the cause and avoid contact with it in the future. If your horse seems distressed or the patches seem severe, call your vet who can prescribe drugs for a speedier recovery.

CHAPTER 11

TACK SORES AND INJURIES

Selecting the right tack is very important, but unless you also know how to fit and use it correctly, you could do more harm than good. There are three good reasons for ensuring that tack fits well and is put on properly. First, well-fitting tack ensures the safety of both horse and rider; secondly, it prevents unnecessary injuries and sores; and thirdly, it will actually do the job for which it is intended. The consequences of ill-fitting tack can be serious.

SORES

A sore which develops as a result of the girth or saddle rubbing is called a **gall.** It is a thickening of the skin caused by constant rubbing and uneven pressure.

The most common sites for **saddle galls** are the withers or the middle of the back along the spine. Sometimes they also appear on either side of the back where the saddle panels cause constant friction.

Girth galls can develop when a soft, flabby horse wears a tough leather girth; or because the girth constantly rubs back and forth while in use; or because the girth is too wide to sit comfortably in the horse's sternum curve.

Most tack-related sores can be prevented:

- Make sure that the tack fits the horse properly – ask a good saddler or experienced instructor if in doubt.
- Ensure that the horse is always clean underneath the tack.
- Keep the tack clean and supple.
- Always check tack once it is on the horse.

Girth galls

A **string girth** can be useful in securing a saddle that slips when using a plain leather girth. However, if it is not fitted carefully it can pinch the skin between the strands and if it is pulled up tightly from one side only it will wrinkle the skin underneath, which leads to discomfort and sores. To ensure that this does not happen, always pull the horse's forelegs gently forward after saddling to make certain that the skin is lying flat underneath.

An **atherstone girth** is shaped behind the shoulder to prevent the problem of pinching but you still need to ensure that the skin is lying flat.

If you suspect that a horse is likely to develop a girth gall (perhaps a

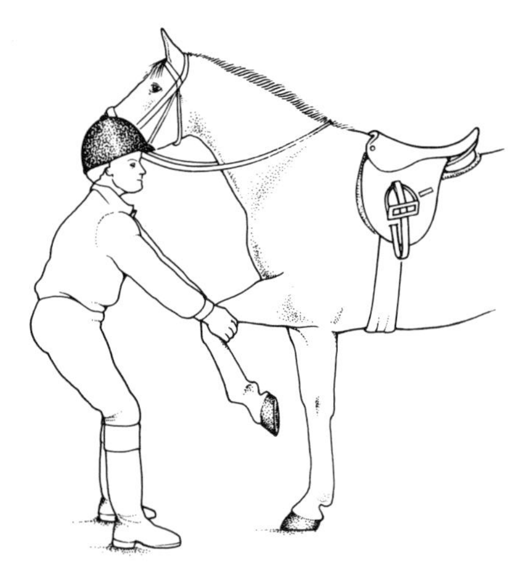

To prevent girth galls, pull your horse's leg gently forward after putting on the saddle and tightening the girth.

horse that has just been brought back into work and is still flabby), take preventive measures. Use a soft cotton girth instead of a tougher leather one, for example, or use a sheepskin girth sleeve which slips over the girth to provide a soft cushion between tack and skin. To harden a horse's skin, surgical spirit or salt water can be rubbed daily into the areas most prone to galling.

SADDLES

Ill-fitting saddles can be very painful for the horse and no horse should be expected to put up with such discomfort. In mild cases the horse may develop back pain and in more severe cases may develop nasty sores where the saddle has been constantly rubbing back and forth. To prevent such injuries, always use a qualified saddler to fit the saddle to the horse – and reassess the situation continually, because horses change shape according to the work that they are doing (and so do riders). In many cases the saddle can be reflocked to ensure a correct fit, but if the saddle cannot be 'set up' to fit exactly, or if your original saddle cannot be adapted to a new horse's shape, then it will have to be changed.

You can always tell if a horse has had a saddle sore as the hair usually grows back white. To encourage the horse's normal coat colour to grow back, rub in coconut oil three times daily as soon as the sore develops.

When fitting a saddle, always ensure that, when viewed from behind, you can see daylight through to the pommel and that you can place four fingers (three if you are mounted) between the horse's withers and the pommel. Also check that the saddle does not pinch the horse on either side of the withers, behind the shoulders. To make sure of a good fit, always carry out such tests both dismounted and mounted.

If you use a numnah or shock-absorbing foam under the saddle, make sure that it is pulled well up into the gullet of the saddle or it will slip down, putting pressure on the spine and possibly causing sores. Badly chosen and poorly fitted numnahs can have the adverse effects of overheating a horse's back and wrinkling, which is a common cause of sores. Additionally, if the saddle is just on the borderline of being too tight, then a numnah will make it tighter.

BITS

Bits can cause a lot of damage, or, rather, it is not the bits themselves

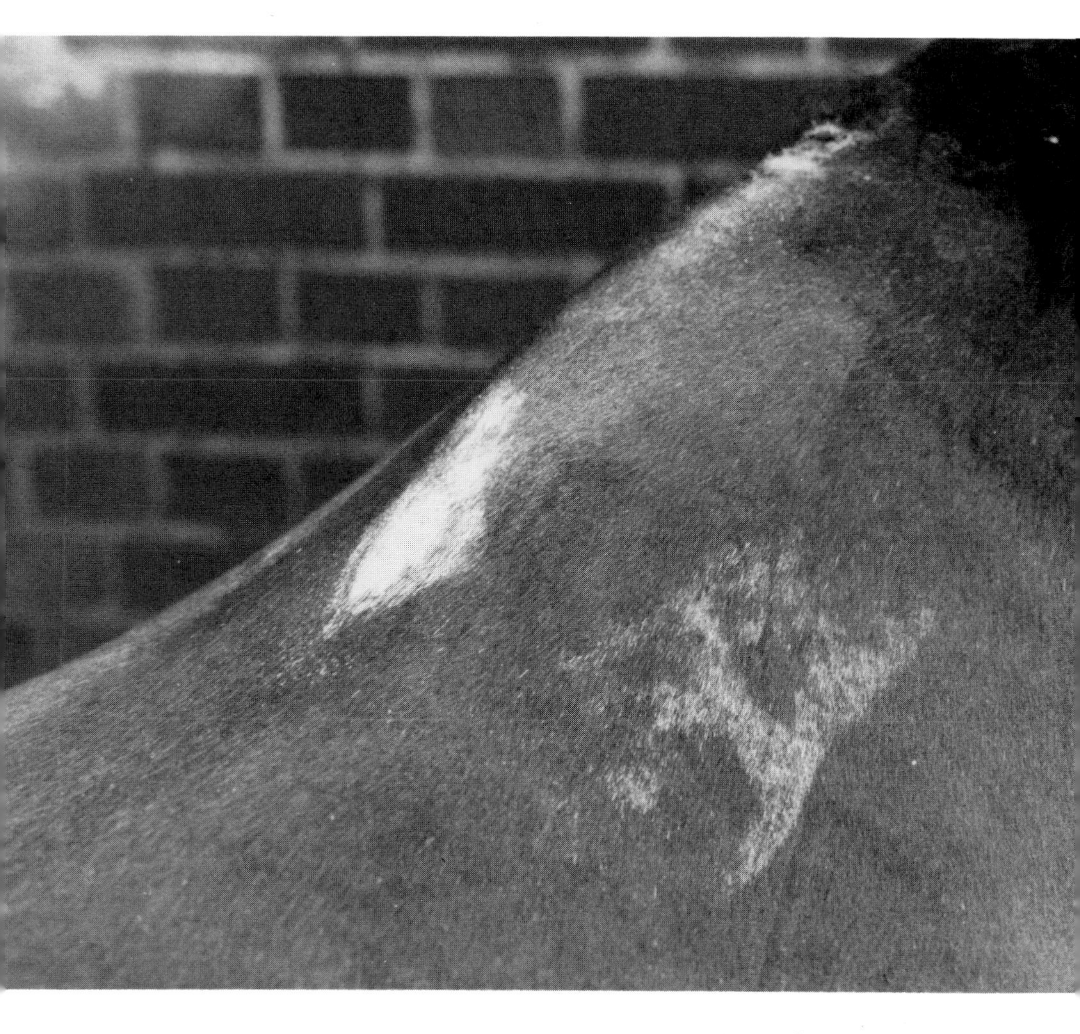

White patches show that this horse has at some time been subjected to an ill-fitting saddle.

but the people who select and fit them and the hands on the other ends of the reins which cause the damage. It is essential to fit a bit properly if it is to offer maximum effect and comfort and to check that the horse's mouth is comfortable (see p. 22).

Before putting any bit into a horse's mouth, check that there are no sores and that the teeth are not sharp. When a horse is being 'mouthed' (a term used for introducing a horse to a bit), extreme care must be taken in fitting the bit so as not to cause discomfort, otherwise the horse will reject the bit, fighting against its action, and is then on the way to becoming 'hard mouthed'. A fulmer snaffle is a good choice for this job as it offers a guiding action.

With a correctly fitting snaffle bit, no more than about a centimetre (½in) should project on either side

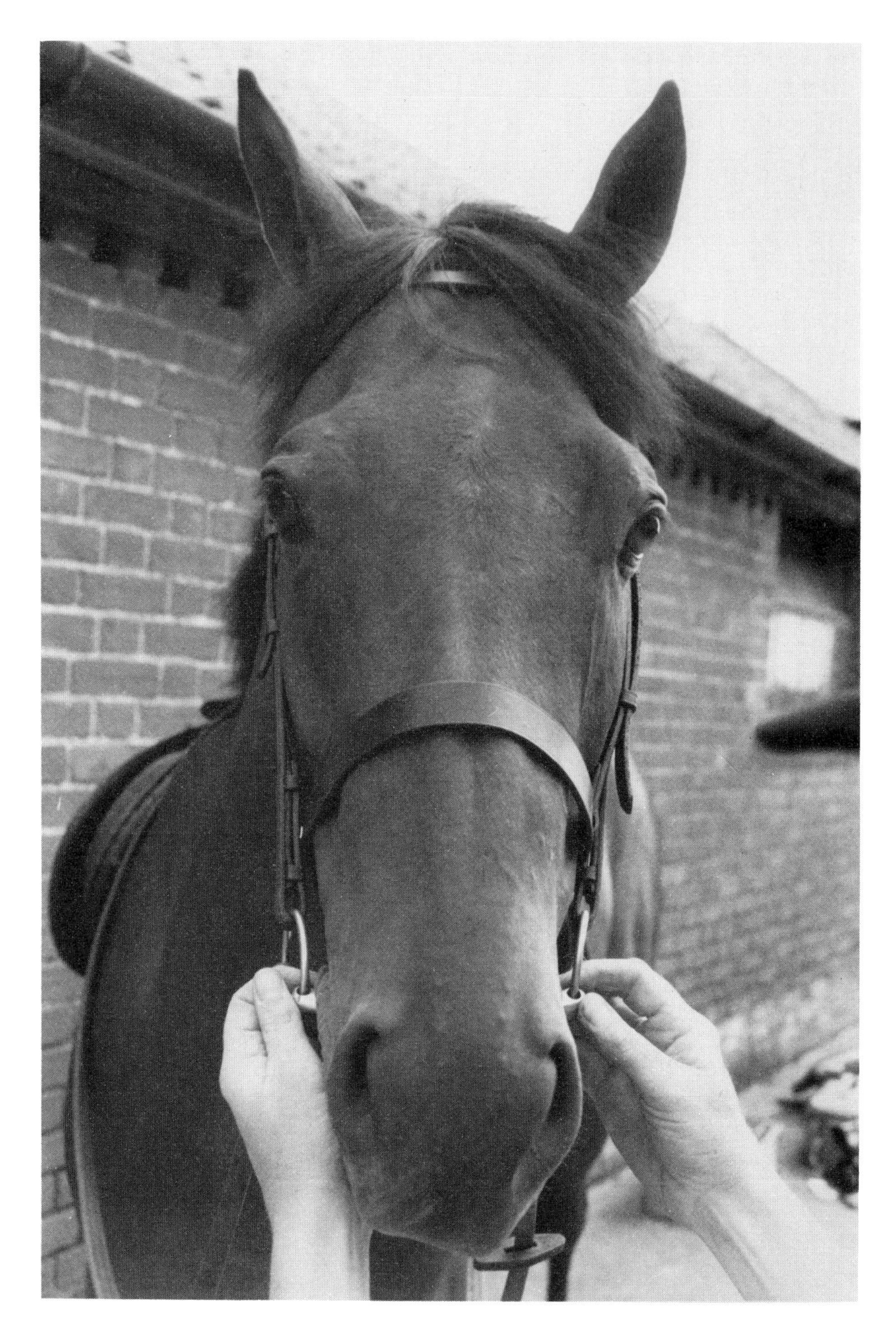

To prevent sores, always check to see that a horse's tack fits properly and is adjusted correctly.

and the corners of the mouth should be slightly wrinkled.

Extreme care must be taken when fitting the bits of a double bridle. The bridoon should be slightly higher in the mouth than a normal snaffle, where a positive wrinkle can be seen. The curb is suspended about 2.5cm (1in) below this to prevent the bits crossing over and to help keep the curb chain in the chin groove when in use.

Typical tell-tale signs of bit damage are pink marks around the corners of the lips, which were probably caused by someone pulling too hard on the bit or a bit which was too small.

THE HORSE AT GRASS

A horse turned out can still be subjected to tack injuries. Where a horse wears a New Zealand rug, be sure to check that it is not rubbing the withers and chest areas. If there are signs of rubbing, sew in some sheepskin to protect these areas. Similarly, a horse that is turned out in a headcollar should have it removed and the face and headcollar cleaned each day, or else the mud will build up and rub on the face.

POOR PERFORMANCE

A horse in pain cannot perform well. Instead of concentrating on your wishes, his mind can only focus on the pain he receives each time you move in the saddle or use the reins. If you are not aware of the underlying problems you may punish your horse mistakenly, which may result in him resisting you even more. In all cases where a horse's behaviour is not as usual when ridden, you should first consider the tack and the horse's health as possible causes.

Tack can also be used to prevent injuries. A common example is when travelling: horses wear travelling equipment to prevent them banging and rubbing themselves while in the horsebox, which all helps to ensure that they perform well on the day.

TREATMENT

In many cases the only treatment for tack injuries is rest – you cannot put the offending item back on the horse. However, with new technology and more training methods becoming available to the horse owner, there are alternatives. An unridden horse's fitness can be maintained by swimming, which will also help to massage and clean the affected areas.

Animal physiotherapists are increasingly playing an important role in equine sports fitness. They have many machines at their disposal which help to aid repair of a damaged area and they are able to advise how to prevent such problems from recurring.

CHAPTER 12

EMERGENCIES

ROAD ACCIDENTS

This is one of the most harrowing situations you might find yourself in. While you will obviously never plan to be in or witness a riding accident on the road, you should be prepared to deal with the situation should it ever occur. First, ensure that the rider is unhurt, or administer first aid if it is needed. If you do not already know how to perform first aid and check for broken bones, or how to put an unconscious person into the recovery position, for example, then you should take a first aid course.

If the horse is loose, he will be scared, so be gentle and reassuring when trying to catch him. Having caught him, check him over for signs of injuries. If these are great call the emergency services and ask for the police, who will contact the nearest available vet. If the horse is bleeding, try to stop this by firmly holding a clean pad (a handkerchief, for example) over the wound. If the horse is on the ground, rest his head on a coat or jumper. As he may have broken some bones, try to restrain him from getting up: kneel on his neck just below his head. Sometimes blindfolding a horse with a coat over the head is enough to keep him still.

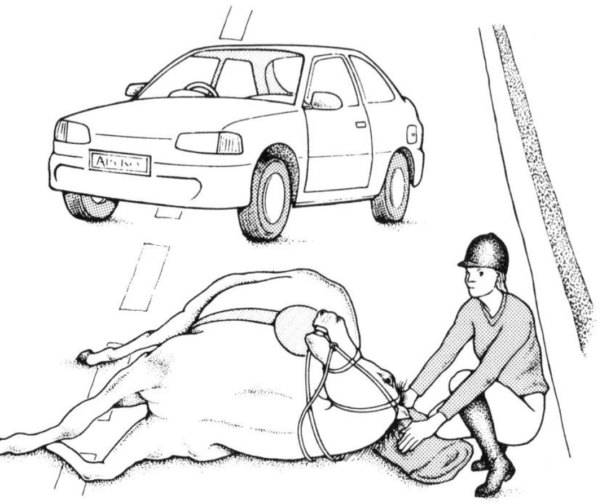

If a horse injured in a road accident is lying down, don't force him to get up. Ask someone to summon a vet as a matter of urgency.

Always ride carefully when on the roads to help prevent road accidents.

Even if the horse is unhurt he will probably be suffering from shock (see p. 91) so put put a coat or a blanket over him to keep him warm. If it is your own horse which has been injured, get him home (preferably in a horsebox) as soon as possible after the vet has attended him, and keep a very keen eye on him for the next week or so.

So that you are prepared at all times when riding, carry a few essential items in your pocket:

- A fold-up hoof pick.
- Some money for the telephone.
- A bandage.
- A clean handkerchief.
- A lead rope clipped to your saddle.
- Your name, address and telephone number inside your hat.
- Written details of any illness suffered, or an identity bracelet which gives such information.

To help prevent accidents from occurring in the first place, make sure you can be seen at all times. Always wear bright clothes, preferably fluorescent ones which can be clearly seen from a distance. If riding far from home, carry reflective bands with you in your pocket so that you can put them on if caught out when the light is fading. If you know that you are likely to be out when it starts to get dark, make sure that you wear a stirrup light showing white to the front and red to the rear.

At all times you should keep a clear head: do not panic as this will only lead to accidents.

STABLE FIRES

Dealing with a horse in a stable fire is terrifying, but for the horse's sake you must act sensibly and positively. **First, call the emergency services.** Do *not* attempt to rescue the horse yourself if this means putting your own or other lives at risk.

Your first thought will be to get the horse out, but remember that he will be extremely anxious and will probably be very strong. If you can get at his headcollar (a good reason for leaving every horse's headcollar outside his box), put it on and lead him away to the safety of the field or try to get someone else to hold him if there are other horses to rescue. If you cannot get his headcollar, use a belt or scarf, but be extra careful. A horse that sees fire in front of him may refuse to come out of the stable and you must quickly decide what to do. In this situation blindfolding him is probably the answer. Use your coat or a damp sheet. Once your horse cannot see, he will have to put his trust in you and follow you.

Having got him away from danger do not let him loose just to get him away from the fire as he may be so upset that he might run on to the road and cause an accident or get hurt himself. Some horses will even run back into the burning stables.

After the rescue, try to keep the horse calm and reassure him by talking constantly. He may be suffering from shock, so keep him warm. Ask your vet to take a look at him, just to make sure that he has not suffered from the smoke or the frightening experience, and keep a vigilant eye on him for the next week or so.

Blindfolding may be the only way to keep a horse calm or to get him to follow you in an emergency situation such as a fire.

THE CAST HORSE

This is another frightening occasion when you will need to stay calm and act positively. A cast horse is one who has lain down in the stable and cannot get up because he has rolled over and ended up too close to the wall and it is more likely to happen if the stable is too small.

The first thing you must do is to decide whether you can move the horse yourself. Are you strong enough? Is it possible to shift him from his current position? Will you frighten him more by trying to do so? If you cannot do it alone, *quickly* summon help. The horse is likely to panic when you leave, if he thinks you are not going to return, so hurry.

If it is a small pony which is stuck, or if you are particularly strong, you can probably help the horse yourself. Sometimes you might only need to pull the horse's front legs forward in order for him to be able to jump up on his own, as he would naturally. If you cannot swing him around without causing further damage, you will need to use a couple of lungeing reins to assist you. Pass one around the horse's hindleg, and one around the foreleg, just above the fetlocks, on the side closest to the wall. Then gently pull on the ropes so that the horse rolls over on his back, until his feet touch down on your side. Move aside hastily and allow the horse to jump up on his own. He may be frightened, so reassure him while clearing away

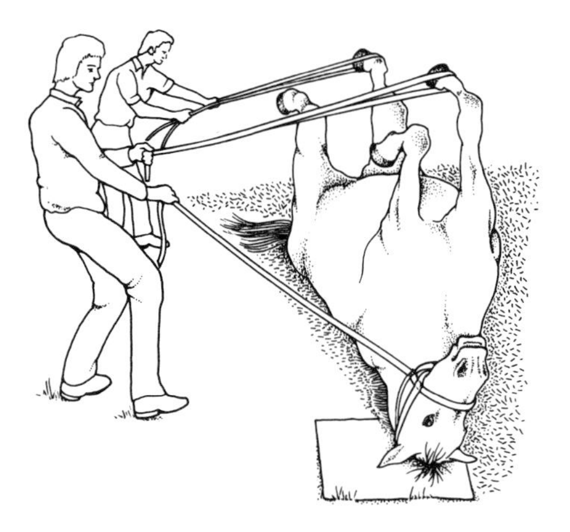

How to turn a cast horse safely.

the reins. Check that he is not injured and stay with him until he is settled.

Some horses are more prone to getting cast than others. For these it is a sensible precaution to use an anti-cast roller, which prevents the horse from rolling right over.

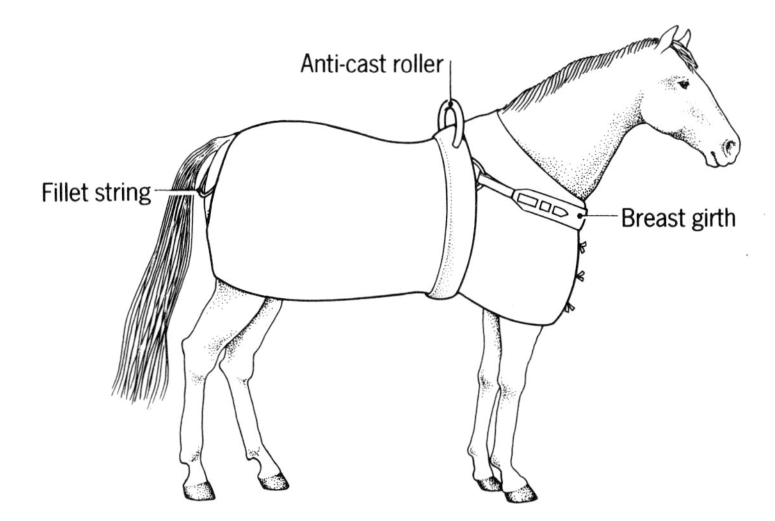

An anti-cast roller will help to prevent a horse from becoming cast.

THE HORSE IN SHOCK

Having endured any of the previous situations, a horse is likely to be in shock. If the horse looks depressed, feel the coat – is it cold to touch? If you suspect shock you should investigate further.

- Take your horse's temperature: it may be *lower* than normal.
- Take a look at the mucous membranes: they may have taken on a bluish tinge.
- Take the pulse: it may be rapid, but weak.

Call your vet immediately. While waiting, get the horse into a nice warm stable. Warmth is crucial: put on dry rugs and stable bandages or use infra-red lights.

The horse need not necessarily have been in an emergency to suffer shock. There are many other causes such as colic, diarrhoea or severe injury which can also result in shock.

METHODS OF RESTRAINT

There may be times when you need to deal with something quickly, yet a horse is not co-operative.

If the situation requires the horse to stand still, try holding up a front foot, or pinching a section of skin, or twitching the horse. In severe cases, where the horse will not stand under any circumstances, doping may be necessary. This might seem drastic, but in an emergency there is no time to wait about until the horse complies.

LIAISING WITH PROFESSIONALS

Whenever there has been an emergency, it is important to liaise with the appropriate professionals to get further advice. While you may have got your horse away from a fire, for example, and may even have been able to put the fire out, you need to establish that your horse has not

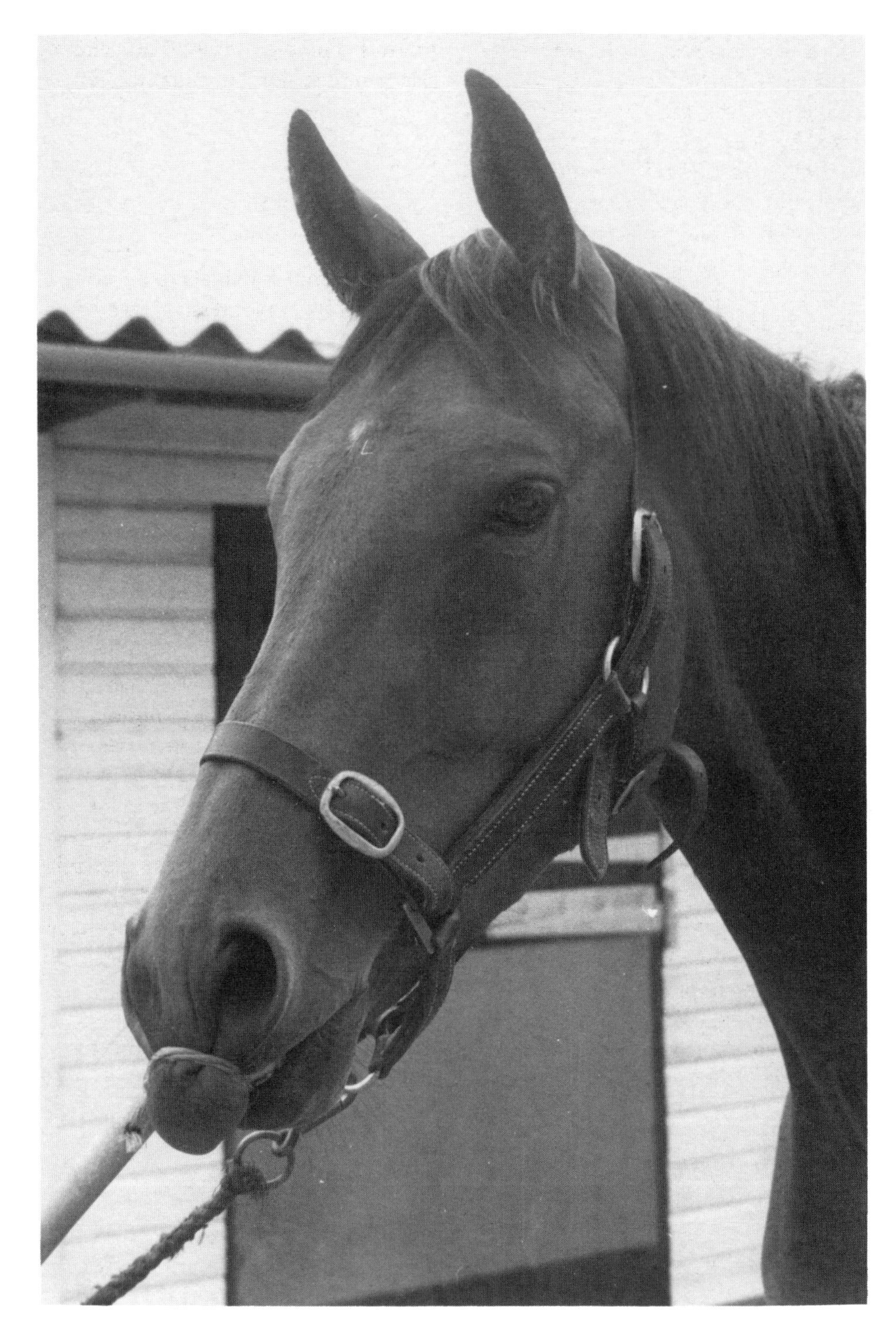

Twitching is a common and effective method of restraint when a horse is less than co-operative.

suffered and you need to determine the cause of the fire: your horse will need to see a vet, and the stables should be checked by a member of the fire brigade. This follow-up is important: it may prevent such incidents from happening again. The safest policy is to have annual visits by appropriate professionals. For instance, do you know whether any mice have been chewing your electricity cables recently? 'If in doubt – check it out.'

OLD AGE – COPING WITH LIFE'S END

Your horse is a much loved friend, with whom you have shared many wonderful memories, and you never want to think about a time when he may no longer be with you. The most satisfactory end is where your old horse gently slips away in his paddock. Although losing him will never be easy, it does help if you know that he has had a good life and that he died peacefully.

More traumatic is having to decide whether it is fair to keep your horse alive with the quality of life that he has. Deciding to put your horse down is never easy, but letting your horse suffer because you cannot face up to the fact that it is best to let him go, is unkind. The biggest factor in making the right decision is evaluating his quality of life:

- Is he in pain?
- Is he constantly on drugs to relieve the pain?
- Is his condition likely to improve, or will it get progressively worse?
- Is he old and very stiff?
- Does he find walking difficult?
- Does he find eating difficult?
- Does he keep suffering from one complaint after another?
- If you have to sell him, is he going to a kind, caring home – do you *really* know?

While your vet will advise whether euthanasia is the kindest option if your horse is suffering from an illness, especially if he is in pain, only you will know whether it is time to let your horse go gracefully if he is simply getting old. It is an extremely difficult decision to make, but it is often kinder to have your horse put down at home rather than pass him on to another home which might abuse him. You do owe your horse that much for the years of enjoyment he may have given you.

INDEX